BETWEEN THE LINES
TONY CLARK'S
DOSSIER

Krystyna Zukowska

B☘XTREE

ACKNOWLEDGEMENTS

I would like to thank Carol Ann Docherty at Island World for all her help in getting this book off the ground; Blackjacks for sorting out all the computer disks; Juliet Haw for help with the typing; Stella and Nigel Clark for their enthusiasm, support and drinks, and Rod Green for everything else.

First published in Great Britain in 1994 by
Boxtree Limited · Broadwall House · 21 Broadwall · London SE1 9PL

10 9 8 7 6 5 4 3 2 1

Book and cover design by Martin Lovelock
Cover photograph of Tony Clark © BBC 1994
Cover Photograph by Pete Jones
Photographs supplied by BBC Photograph Library and Archive

Printed and bound in Great Britain by Redwood Books, Wiltshire
A CIP catalogue entry for this book is available from the British Library.

ISBN: 0-7522-0984-1

YOU ARE A DEAD MAN CLARK YOU HAVE MADE ME SUFFER AND NOW IT IS YOUR TURN YOU WILL NEVER KNOW WHEN I WILL STRIKE, MAYBE TODAY, MAYBE TOMORROW, MAYBE NEXT YEAR KEEP LOOKING OVER YOUR SHOULDER I AM COMING AFTER YOU

The Purpose Of This Report

The letter you saw on the previous page is one of several I have received recently, all of which say more or less the same thing. My days are numbered; my time is up; I'm heading for that great Interview Room in the sky. I have tried not to take the letters seriously. Death threats are, after all, spat in the face of most coppers when they have to deal with drunken brawlers, or drag some spaced-out crackhead into the back of a police van. These letters, though, have started to prey on my mind. They are delivered by hand, so the culprit has gone to the trouble of finding out where I live and, presumably, takes the risk of stuffing them through my letter-box personally in order to let me know that he - or she - has been standing right there on my doorstep. In the past, even that might not have been enough to get me really worried, but raking back over the embers of some of my cases has made me realise just how many people there are in this world who would seriously want to see me dead. The out-and-out villains can be terrifying enough, but the sly and devious schemers who played the corruption game and lost are more worrying still. Given time to brood and calculate their revenge, the schemers are the most dangerous breed of all. The following reports are written up from case notes, and form my own list of suspects.

Suspect Dossier file No.:1
Subject: PATRICK SALTER

Superintendent Patrick Salter was a man whose attention and favour I had always courted during my time at Mulberry Street nick. He was a superior officer of great influence who had the ear of the high command, and as such he was a man I had always hoped to impress. He wasn't very impressed when I arrested him.

Salter had the dubious distinction of being the first serving police officer I had ever collared. I think that it was almost as disconcerting a situation for me as it was for him. It was shortly after my promotion to Superintendent that the whole world started spinning in a different direction. I had grand dreams of joining the Flying Squad and hitting the fast track to Chief Superintendent in a blaze of glory with a clutch of high-profile cases under my belt. I had an informal interview lined up at New Scotland Yard with a view to transferring to the Squad. Confirmation of my posting seemed like it would just be a formality. It certainly didn't work out that way.

The last case I worked on at Mulberry Street was a drugs bust. I led a raid on the home of Thomas MacMurray – a known heroin dealer. The raid had been meticulously planned. We were going in on the weekend of the Notting Hill Carnival, a weekend when MacMurray would know that our troops were spread pretty thin on the ground and when he would certainly not be expecting an early morning call – only he was. Along with one of my mates, DI Mickey Flynn, and his bagman, Sergeant Paul Tanner, I was one of the first through the door and the smirk on MacMurray's face as he was dragged out of bed said it all. The house was clean. The only thing we caught him with was a Silk Cut.

I remember trying to shake off the feelings of frustration and concentrate my mind when I arrived at the Yard the following day for my informal interview with the Flying Squad – but I had another shock coming. When I walked into his office, my interviewer walked out, leaving behind Commander Huxtable and Chief Superintendent Deakin. I thought even then that Deakin was a cold bastard. They told me they were from the Complaints Investigation Bureau – CIB – and that far from being promoted I was under suspicion of corruption. But they weren't officially investigating me and they weren't taping the interview – it was 'just another informal chat'. Their attention had been drawn to the situation at Mulberry Street by a disgruntled informant named Spence, who claimed that there were bent coppers on offer there.

Andy Spence was a small-time pill peddler from the Marchmain Estate. As well as dabbling in drugs he was also a registered informant. Mickey Flynn and Paul Tanner used him all the time – it was a rough estate which saw a lot of action, and they needed to be kept in the know. Spence had recently taken exception to the somewhat heavy-handed treatment he had received from Flynn and Tanner, and he also had a grudge against MacMurray, and these two things had sent him running to the CIB. Sitting in the back of their car, he told Detective Sergeant Maureen Connell and DI Harry Naylor that someone was on the take down at Mulberry Street. And where was I? At Mulberry Street. I was immediately under suspicion, along with the other senior management at the station: Superintendent Pat Salter and Chief Superintendent Dave Pollock. Mickey Flynn was also under suspicion; it was, after all, his snout who went running to the CIB, screaming police corruption.

Spence alleged that some officer at Mulberry Street was tipping off the major drug supplier in the area as to when all the police raids were going down. Subsequently, every time a raid was carried out, the big drugs players were never there. Huxtable and Deakin had a very simple proposition to put to me. Investigate Spence's allegations and find out who was responsible, or I could kiss my transfer goodbye. They had not, of course, ruled out the possibility that I might be involved, but I was ideally placed to become their mole at Mulberry Street. If I came up with nothing, they could still abandon subtlety and wade straight in. Undoubtedly, I would get caught up in the crossfire and the transfer would be gone, but if I delivered the goods, their implication was that a transfer would be waiting for me at the end of the rainbow. I had to infiltrate my own nick.

Although those raids had been planned down to the last detail, the troops at Mulberry Street never knew when they were going to be pulled off – they only found out at the last minute, to minimise the risks of leaks. The only people who were meant to know in advance of the raid on MacMurray's place were myself, Mickey Flynn and Superintendent Salter, which certainly seemed to narrow things down a bit.

I started the investigation by interviewing the informant, Andy Spence. He was being held in a safe house by DI Naylor and DS Connell, with whom I would work closely throughout the investigation. He was in the safe house for his own good – too many people were out to get him, from both sides of the law. My good mates Flynn and Tanner were gunning for him as they suspected he had warned Thomas MacMurray of our raid – or at least knew the man who did. And Thomas MacMurray was after him as he knew Spence had gone to CIB in revenge for MacMurray having dumped his services as a go-between and dealing direct with the heroin supplier.

I asked Spence how information about police raids filtered down to him. He had been conspicuously absent from recent raids at the Black Horse pub and the Marigold Club. He wasn't saying, but I knew the tip-offs had to be coming from the heroin baron who supplied MacMurray. I needed a name. Andy wasn't being a great deal of help, and just as I was about to give him a really hard time, he did a runner from the safe house. I tracked him down a few days later – reckon I did him a favour as he was just about to be pulped by Flynn and Tanner, still furious about the MacMurray fiasco. I charged in like a knight in shining armour and rescued him from the clutches of my two colleagues. This time Spence agreed to talk – and gave me what I wanted.

The heroin supplier's name was Paul Lucas. He had begun his career in the 1980s. In those days it was only minor drug offences but he soon graduated to the harder stuff, dealing in heroin. There was nothing to connect him direct to Mulberry Street, but then Mo – Maureen Connell – uncovered something very interesting. Back in 1987 or 1988 Paul Lucas had acted as an informant for the Drugs Squad. He was handled by a Chief Inspector who returned to uniform after his promotion to Superintendent. His name was Patrick Salter. And I was going out with him that evening.

A few days before, Salter had rather unexpectedly invited me and my then-wife, Sue, to his Lodge's annual Ladies' Night dance. I was a bit surprised: he had never been that chummy before, but I guessed that's what happened when you got promoted and went to play with the big boys. I remember I didn't say yes immediately – I never did as in those days I had to clear these things with Sue. Anyway, it was a good opportunity to get to know the man better – and he turned out to be full of surprises. For one thing, he couldn't do enough for me, suggesting I meet his investment adviser and offering a tidy sum to help me throw in my lot with his investment syndicate, no strings attached. For another, it seemed his wife collected hair salons like other people collect CDs. She told Sue she had three, had her eye on a fourth, and invited both of us to join them for a week in their villa in Portugal. She confided to Sue in the ladies that she wasn't a great businesswoman, but her husband was a wonderful accountant. He would have to be. He sure as hell wasn't getting all that money for investment from a copper's salary.

Anyway, it was worth checking out the salon – and Harry, Mo and I weren't disappointed. Business was brisk; a lot of money was changing hands. It was an ideal set-up either for laundering drugs money or for accepting corrupt payments, or both. Then we got really lucky. We spotted Sheila Curry entering the salon. She was a nice woman: elegant looking, slim figure, well-spoken, but was known as a meeter and greeter of mules – drugs couriers – off the planes at Heathrow. Sheila herself had no problem with heroin, but just couldn't resist coke, which meant she kept some pretty unsavoury company. When we dug a little deeper into her background we found she was living with Paul Lucas.

The next step was easy: I sprung the trap. Over lunch with Patrick Salter I told him I was on to something big but I didn't want it to go any further: I was targeting Paul Lucas and was planning to get him. I didn't have to wait long for results. The following day we followed Lucas to Heathrow where he boarded a plane, waved off by his loving girlfriend Sheila. My quiet word in Salter's ear had gone straight back to Lucas. Salter was our man, all right.

We followed Sheila back to her flat and on inspection uncovered quite a few goodies – £6,000 in used low-denomination notes, and cocaine in the dental floss dispenser. Sheila was, if nothing else, an inventive girl. She was intelligent too: she didn't want to go to prison, so we set up a deal. In return for us turning a blind eye to her bad choice of boyfriend and favourite pastime, she would deliver the £6,000, now carefully marked, as originally planned. We followed her by car to Carol Salter's hair salon. Then we waited. A few minutes later Salter arrived with a briefcase, all ready to pick up his cut of the sale of Lucas's heroin, as well as the payments made to him by the dealer in exchange for information on drugs raids planned by our Mulberry Street lot. The whole thing stank.

When I arrested Patrick Salter at the bank where he planned to deposit his payments I was happy I'd cornered the corrupt bastard. In my eyes, in just a few days, Salter had gone from being someone whose respect and endorsement I had craved, to being no more than any other slag off the streets. In fact, he was worse than any ordinary villain. He had abused the responsibility that goes with the uniform and what's more, he hadn't even made things particularly difficult for us. I felt he had betrayed me and every other honest cop. Nobody else down at Mulberry Street station saw me as an avenging angel, though. I'd put away their boss and made a lot of enemies as a result – Flynn and Tanner couldn't even look me in the eye.

If I'd lost some mates, Salter had lost a lot more. His house, the villa in Portugal and his wife's businesses – all his assets – were judged to have come from drugs money and seized. He'd lost his job, his respect in the community and his freedom. Life for a former police officer is none too pleasant inside one of Her Majesty's establishments. In the 'Who Wants Tony Clark Dead Stakes', Salter is up there with the front runners.

And my reward for my part in all this? My dreamed promotion took me not into the hallowed halls of the Flying Squad, but straight into the welcoming arms of CIB and Chief Superintendent John Deakin. For the foreseeable future, I was to be policing the police, and I was to pick up a lot more enemies along the way.

Suspect Dossier file No.:2
Subjects: MICHAEL BRANDLE &
CHIEF SUPERINTENDENT JAMISON

The business down at Coverdale Road nick was a messy affair. It was the first job that put me squarely in my place – where I learnt that CIB is all about examining bent coppers and leaving investigating and arresting of ordinary villains to the boys at the sharp end. The boys then come under our investigation, of course. However, the incident at Coverdale Road did bring me into contact with two extremely unsavoury characters, each from opposite sides of the law – a nice balance. Michael Brandle was scum of the first division, while Chief Super Jamison of Coverdale Road ... well, there's a man who could wank for England. Both hated my guts by the end of that investigation – and both are unbalanced and stupid enough to try and get me now.

The whole episode began as an investigation into two Armed Response coppers who were a bit hasty with their shooters and apparently shot dead one Michael Brandle on the Sourville Estate. I wish they had done the job properly. No one deserves to be snuffed out more than Michael Brandle, but this case turned out to be as full of cock-ups as a field of randy rabbits. I was called in to head the investigation into PCs Webb and Jelkes from the Armed Response team – to determine why they had shot the man and to make sure that they had followed the correct procedures every step of the way.

Deakin filled me in on the background to the incident. At 6.30 am a call came through to Coverdale Road; an unidentified caller informed the duty officer, Inspector Tom Reith, that a madman brandishing a gun was attempting to gain access into a flat – number 28, we later found out – on the Sourville Estate. Two officers from Coverdale Road – PCs Farrow and Moreford – were the first to arrive on the scene and they radioed back to the station, confirming the informant's story. Because of the unstable behaviour of the gunman, and because he had a gun clearly visible in his hand in a residential area, the Armed Response team was called in. At 6.50 am the ARV arrived at the Sourville Estate, where Constables Jelkes and Webb were ordered to cover the gunman. They took up positions either side of the target on the open walkway outside the flats. They each used the entrances to stairwells as cover, trapping the gunman between them on the walkway, but had to leave themselves dangerously exposed in order to keep their weapons trained on the target. A few minutes later they shot him dead.

So far, so good and simple. But at this point several events occurred which suddenly turned my easy little job into a minefield. First, at the press conference held by Chief Super Jamison of Coverdale Road and my boss, Deakin, the journos began to scent that the gun was a replica. This turned out to be true. Cock-up number one.

Cock-up number two happened when I, along with Mr Lownes from the Police Complaints Authority, went to Brandle's mother's flat on the same estate. We were just offering our sincere condolences, when Michael Brandle walked through the door. I

9

remember thinking that either a miracle had happened or somebody from Coverdale Road had a hell of a lot of explaining to do. As miracles are thin on the ground in places like the Sourville Estate, I went for the second option. Michael's mother was screaming at us, Michael was screaming that the copper bastards had shot his brother Vernon, and I was so confused I just left quickly, promising myself that heads would roll.

As disasters generally come along in threes, I didn't have to wait too long for the final piece of bad news that day. Tuning in to the TV, I saw Counsellor 'Red Eddie' Everett. Sourville was part of his ward, and so there he was in full colour, filling the world in on the shooting on the estate. Just for good measure, he rubbed in the cock-ups involving the replica gun and incorrect identification by the police. He swore to get to the bottom of the incident, which meant that my nice simple case had turned into a political hot potato. Political agitation was the last thing I – or the Sourville Estate – needed at that moment. The pressure was on. I had to get this case sorted out quickly.

Jamison proved to be of no help to me whatsoever – it was obvious he hated me and hated the job I did. The only positive response I got from him was when he told me he wasn't going to allow me to stitch him up like I did the coppers down at Mulberry Street. Nice touch. He went straight to the top of my shit-list.

Because of his lack of co-operation I had to roll my sleeves up and, with Mo's help, do my own searching through files at Coverdale Road. We found the file on the dead man, Vernon Brandle. It made pathetic reading. Born in 1975, his criminal career kicked off in a small way – stealing cars for the hell of it, and Mandrax and cannabis possession, for which he got 200 hours of community service. In 1991 he was charged for assault on a police officer while resisting arrest, while in 1992 it was more drugs. Most recently he had been done for causing an affray, and that case was still pending. The file ended with a report from his social worker, stating he was epileptic and educationally subnormal, with the mental age of a twelve year old. When all this reached the gentlemen of the press, the police would be made to look very bad indeed. What the hell was this sad character doing with a gun, even if it was only a fake one? From the files it was obvious he wasn't big-time; to be honest, he'd hardly even made the small-time stakes. Something was beginning to smell very bad, and I didn't know what. What I do remember is that I didn't get any more from Coverdale Road that day – a brick was delivered through the canteen window, courtesy of the Sourville Estate. No one was hurt, but the glass sprayed everywhere and the uniforms in the canteen weren't too happy about having their steak and kidney seasoned with shards. Feelings were beginning to run high.

My first bit of good luck came the following day when my mate and fellow CIB officer, DS McAllister, came up with a video of the shooting – the whole incident, complete with sound. There was a God after all. It transpired that a young lad from the Sourville Estate, Colin Thurber, had been videotaping his little sister's birthday party. When he heard all the shouting from the opposite flats, he went over to the window and taped that instead. It was more interesting than his sister's party, I suppose. With an eye to the main chance, Thurber had tried to sell the tape to the press, but McAllister's own press contacts had done the decent thing and directed him towards the enterprising Thurber.

I listened to that tape all bloody night. I nearly burst my eardrums straining to hear what Vernon Brandle was saying, but it was worth the effort in the end. I thought I heard him say, 'It isn't real', and the reason he gave for trying to get into the flat was to talk to his ex-girlfriend and see his little boy. I could hardly believe he was saying the gun wasn't real. He was shouting this at two armed policemen and they still shot him. I decided it was time to talk to the two men involved – PC Jelkes and PC Webb.

When Mo and I interviewed Jelkes, he was upset but surprisingly upfront about the whole incident. He admitted he fired first, but it had been a mistake: he was concentrating so hard on covering Vernon Brandle that he didn't see a mess of birdshit on the ground. He slipped and fired accidentally; the shot missed, but a few seconds later he saw the back of Brandle's head come off. Jelkes could only guess that his shot triggered Webb into firing. And Webb's aim was good – two shots got Brandle in the face. I quizzed Jelkes about the 'It's not real' comment. I remember he looked surprised – he had believed the gunman was shouting about the situation, not the gun, which seemed fair comment to me. At the time they thought they had a known armed robber in their sights, a truly ruthless individual with a penchant for violence. They didn't know they were dealing with a man who had never mentally matured past the age of twelve – a panicking child.

Mo and I then interviewed the other PC, George Webb. He looked as though he was just out of nappies, and he obviously hadn't stopped shitting himself since the incident. He admitted to firing two shots on hearing the first one go off and, like Jelkes, had thought Brandle's 'It's not real' related to the situation. Webb had also heard the gunman shouting, 'Where's my key?' Admittedly, that would have been a better way of entering the flat. If Vernon Brandle had had a key, he would have been alive later that day.

These interviews were getting me nowhere, so it was back to Coverdale Road and Chief Superintendent Jamison's hospitality. He excelled himself this time – on our arrival we found the nick looking more like a fortress; the coppers decked out in full riot gear, and Jamison charging around, shouting tactical orders like Napoleon. I thought it was all a bit unnecessary, but guessed he was laying on a special show for CIB. In fact, Red Eddie had been stirring up the natives, and Jamison was gearing up for a potential showdown at Sourville. As usual, he made his position very clear, telling me that if I wanted to go to Sourville I should take one of the armed gladiators with me for protection. The hint wasn't lost on me. Jamison was like a big tomcat: he was clearly marking out his territory – territory I was straying all over. He really couldn't stand it.

He couldn't stop me reviewing the files on Michael Brandle though – and they made very interesting reading. Unlike Vernon, Michael was into some seriously anti-social behaviour: armed robberies at an off-licence and a garage, except that the police could not get sufficient evidence to prosecute because of Brandle's reputation for violence. It seemed that none of the witnesses or his neighbours around the Sourville Estate would give evidence for fear of having their legs broken. The local CID had even attempted to get Brandle by going through his brother, threatening to fit him up for a string of burglaries if he didn't co-operate – but Vernon stayed loyal and kept stumm.

At this point I was beginning to get a few ideas of my own. It seemed too much of a coincidence that Vernon had a convincing replica of a gun while his brother had access to the real thing. I knew the answer lay back at the Sourville Estate. Deciding to pass on the opportunity to enjoy the company of one of Jamison's gladiators, I took Mo and we both went there, to flat number 28. I was sure I'd get my answers there.

The door was opened by a washed-out kid called Julie, who really didn't want to speak to us. We forced our way in, and were greeted with a cosy-looking domestic scene – Michael Brandle bouncing a baby on his knee. Darren. His son. It was all coming together now. I guessed Michael's little game, and put it to him. I got it right; he didn't contradict me once. Unlike his brother, Michael had no concept of family loyalty. It was he who had given the replica gun to Vernon, or at least made sure that Vernon knew where to find it. He then also made sure that Vernon would discover the truth about Darren – that he wasn't his dad but Michael was, and that eighteen months ago, when Vernon had been going out with Julie, Michael had been knocking her off, too. Just as Michael predicted, Vernon went right off the deep end. After raging around for a while, he had stormed off to Julie's flat to have it out with his brother, whom he believed to be hiding out there. A quick anonymous phone call to Coverdale Road, and Michael's plan was complete. Michael Brandle set his brother up good and proper. Jelkes had thought he heard Vernon screaming 'Where's my key?' but he had been mistaken. Vernon was yelling 'Where's Mikey?' Michael Brandle killed his brother as surely as if it had been his finger on the trigger of Webb's Smith and Wesson. He wanted Vernon out of the way so that he could settle in with Julie and their baby.

And then came the bit which really offends me: there was nothing I could do. I'd got the full story and I'd got it right, but I was at Coverdale nick investigating the two Armed Response coppers. Civilians were out of my reach – they weren't my business any more. I swore to Brandle I'd get him some day; that I'd make my story stick so hard that his eyes would water. He just laughed – he knew I couldn't touch him. But he was scared. He'd want me out the way because he knows I haven't forgotten – and he's right. I'll nail the bastard some day – if he doesn't get me first.

But it wasn't quite the end of the Coverdale Road saga. Mo and I left the flat, aiming to drown the taste of the truth with some whisky, to be met by the sight of a torched car. Ours. And then all hell broke loose. The scum from the Sourville Estate, spurred on, it would seem, by Red Eddie, were out looking for trouble. The entire howling mob charged us. I was trying to cover Mo when suddenly Jamison's gladiators came thundering around the corner in full riot gear, truncheons waving. Bringing up the rear was Jamison, standing ramrod straight in the open door of his car like a latter-day Rommel. We had a full-scale riot raging around us and there he was, urging his troops to batter the shit out of the enemy on the estate.

It was Jamison who got Mo and me out of that hell-hole. He knew I'd hate that – having to be grateful to him for getting us out. Just for good measure he truncheoned a kid's head in front of our eyes – restoring law and order his way, you understand. As with Brandle, there was nothing I could do. Chief Super Jamison was a good copper. There was no way I could touch him officially, even for the blatant assault on that hyped-up kid. But also, as with Brandle, I swore I'd get him some day. Who knows? Maybe he'll get to me first. But not if I can help it.

Suspect Dossier file No.:3
Subject: DETECTIVE INSPECTOR DICK CORBETT

I remember the investigation at Beckett Park being a case of open-and-shut and then open again. We thought we had investigated the case thoroughly enough – two coppers, Sergeant Alan Siddons and Constable Mike Hanson, were accused of beating up a prostitute, Mary Shibden. She wasn't pressing charges, however, so there was insufficient evidence against the two men and therefore no case. A waste of time, I thought, when I got Mo to take all the files back to the nick. She was pleased that investigation was over – she thought the blokes at Beckett Park nick were really unpleasant and was glad to be shot of them all, apart from an elderly sergeant called Harry Ross. Ross had been something of a mentor to Mo during her earliest days in the job. He had a real soft spot for her. I think he was genuinely pleased to see how her career had progressed, but then Ross was like that – a genuine bloke. He was coach to the police water polo team and as popular a copper as you were ever likely to meet. With nearly thirty years' service under his belt, he was looking forward to picking up his pension and pottering in his garden. The last thing he needed to do was to start making waves, but his fondness for Mo was to be his undoing. Maybe if he hadn't been quite such a nice guy, things would have worked out differently.

The case was reopened because of political intervention. James Hardcastle, MP, had decided that there was political mileage to be made in championing the cause of cleaning up the police force. He had demanded a meeting with Commander Huxtable and Chief Constable Dunning. Not only was Hardcastle a law-and-order campaigner, but one of his constituents, a Mr Feldman, had witnessed the beating-up of the prostitute outside a pub by the two accused officers – indeed, he had even driven her to the Royal Free Hospital after the attack – and was demanding now that the two men be prosecuted. James Hardcastle had told my bosses that Mr Feldman was an insistent – and reliable – witness.

So we were on the case again. Poor Mo – it was back to the hated Beckett Park mob for her.

I remember filling Deakin in on the details of our original investigation at Beckett Park station. Both Hanson and Siddons had admitted to talking with Mary Shibden, but unsurprisingly both denied brutally beating her up – in direct contradiction of what Mr Feldman was stating. However, I hadn't pursued the investigation any further as Mary Shibden wasn't prepared to make a statement and had now disappeared – we assumed she had returned to the North, from where we believed she had originally come. Unfortunately, Deakin wasn't satisfied with the results of my investigation. I knew why he was being so jumpy. It was obvious that he was being pressurised from above to get results; because of the political squeeze being applied by Hardcastle we either had to convict the two officers or exonerate them entirely, to show the public at large that the system of law and order was in fine working order.

I decided that the most sensible place to start would be by finding and interviewing Mary Shibden. If we could get her to talk, her version of events would most probably be the correct one – I hadn't much faith in the story told by Siddons and Hanson. It was, however, an extremely well-rehearsed story and both officers had the backing of all the important men down at Beckett Park station. In fact, if the canteen gossip was to be believed, then the lads there were all brothers together at the local Masonic Lodge. If this was so, then we were going to have huge difficulties breaking into such a tight, closed bunch.

Harry and I spent one illuminating evening down at King's Cross, asking an assortment of women if they knew Mary Shibden's whereabouts. It turned out that she had been seen briefly, but had vanished again, as we had suspected, back up to her home town, Leeds. Poor kid – I felt sorry for her already. She was one of the thousands who flock to London believing that the streets of the capital are paved with gold, only to find that they're full of shit. I decided to send Mo along to find her, as I thought maybe another woman would stand a better chance of having a successful chat with Mary. If what Feldman alleged was true, then it wouldn't surprise me if Mary never wanted to talk to a policeman again.

Meanwhile, I had set up interviews down at CIB headquarters with Siddons and Hanson – again. They knew their story off by heart – but then they had had ample practice over the past six months to get it absolutely right. Siddons told me that the reason he had spoken with Mary in the first place was in connection with the whereabouts of some stolen property. He believed she knew where it could be found as her pimp, one Amal Kabir, had a brother – Mamoud – who was a well-known fence, handling stolen goods on a truly industrial scale. Siddons had reckoned there was a good chance that Mary would know where Mamoud's warehouse was, which is why he and Hanson had sought her out. They had interviewed her in the street because if they had taken her down to the station for questioning her pimp would have suspected she was stitching up his brother – and would then have cut her to ribbons. I remember Harry and I looking at each other, thinking that these boys were all heart.

However, their stories matched and there was nothing we could do but let them go. Word rapidly got back to me that their boss, DI Dick Corbett, was furious that his lads were being questioned again – without his permission – over a case which should have died a long time ago. I remember meeting Dick Corbett and disliking him on sight. He was big and brash, one of those men who seem to sweat constantly. He looked like a bully. It didn't take me long to find out that he actually *was* a bully – and Lodge Master of the local Freemasons, to boot. He was obviously the top dog down at Beckett Park Police Station.

Not having had any joy from interviewing Siddons or Hanson, I thought it was high time I spoke with Feldman – the man primarily responsible for the case being reopened. I knew Deakin had spoken to him already and had come away not liking the man very much. Feldman had asked him whether he had come simply to pacify him and make him feel that his MP was doing a good job. I could see how that attitude would really get up Deakin's nose. Anyway, I had arranged to interview Feldman at his own house. He was elderly, Jewish, and obviously deeply suspicious of the police, but by now I was getting used to everyone mistrusting me. I talked to him about the incident, and showed him photos of Siddons and Hanson for positive identification.

That's when the bombshell exploded. Feldman could only identify one of the men. This most reliable witness could only positively identify one of the men who had beaten up Mary Shibden, yet we knew there were two coppers involved. I was beginning to wonder what the hell was going on when the second bombshell burst. In my Beckett Park file I carried photographs of all senior personnel at the station. Feldman saw them and positively identified the second officer he had seen beating up Mary Shibden. It was Dick Corbett. We now had our evidence. We had proof that both Siddons and Hanson had been lying. I took a statement from Feldman.

More news awaited me back at the office. Mo had rung from Leeds – she had been successful in finding and talking to Mary Shibden, and her story made interesting listening. I had been right about sending Mo – by all accounts Mary had opened up to her. She had told Mo that she was stoned on the night she was beaten up by the two coppers. She was always getting knocked about anyway, so what did anything matter? ... Mary then asked Mo to turn off the tape. Off the record, she told Mo that Siddons and Hanson were the two monkeys, but the organ-grinder who controlled them was Dick Corbett. She confirmed that it was Corbett and Hanson who had confronted her; that on that night Siddons was nowhere in sight but had embraced the given story to protect his boss. But that wasn't all of Mary's information. Three days after Feldman had made his complaint against her police attackers, Corbett tracked her down and took her into Beckett Park Police Station. There he put her in an empty cell, kicked the shit out of her, broke her jaw and then told her to get out of London. Convinced as to the seriousness of his intentions, she did as she was ordered.

Damning as this all was, it amounted to nothing without some kind of corroboration from someone at Beckett Park. We knew it wouldn't be easy to get anyone to talk. What we didn't realise was how everyone at Beckett Park closed ranks. Despite being confronted with Feldman's sworn statement, Corbett denied having been anywhere near Mary either in the street or in the cells, while everyone else at Beckett Park mysteriously underwent a form of collective amnesia and couldn't remember ever having seen Mary Shibden down in the police cells. Even Mo's questioning of Harry Ross, the custody sergeant on duty the night Mary's jaw was broken, failed to produce results. His custody records for that evening showed no sign of Mary Shibden having enjoyed his hospitality, and he knew nothing about any tom being given a pasting in the cells. Mo's favourite wasn't talking either.

If the softly-softly tactic wasn't working, I decided we had to get tough. Harry Ross was brought in for questioning at our offices. Mo and I interviewed him together. Not surprisingly he kept evading the Mary Shibden question, palming us off with the comment that if he had known that she was lying injured in the cells then he would have sent for a doctor or ambulance. Mo asked him if it was common knowledge at Beckett Park that Siddons was covering up for Corbett so the DI's name wouldn't be dragged into the investigation, thus ruining his chances of a forthcoming promotion. Again, our bird wasn't singing. I had had enough. I switched off the tape recorder and left the room for a cup of tea. Later on that evening, Mo told me that after I'd left Harry Ross admitted to her that Detective Inspector Dick Corbett had beaten up prostitute Mary Shibden in the police cells at Beckett Park Police Station. Ross had turned a blind eye while Corbett did his dirty work, but he had a reputation as an honest man – an honest copper – and his lifetime in uniform was, ultimately, worth more to him than the comradeship of scum like Corbett. He had been struggling with a classic dilemma: keep his conscience clear, speak up and crucify Corbett, but risk losing his standing amongst those for whom he cared most; or keep his mouth shut, stay loyal to his Masonic brothers, but live beneath the shadow of guilt for the rest of his days. In the end he had chosen to be true to himself.

Harry's statement, together with Feldman's, meant that the Department of Public Prosecutions could now prosecute Corbett, plus the other two officers, Siddons and Hanson. We had a result. It was fireproof.

The business didn't end there, however. Corbett and his team were never prosecuted. So much for being fireproof – I had forgotten about bloody bad luck. Our chief witness, Mr Feldman, went out one morning on his bicycle, suffered an enormous heart attack and died. Without him, the rest of the case just didn't stand up. Harry Ross, meanwhile, by becoming a turncoat and telling the truth to Mo, was ostracised by all of his old mates down at Beckett Park. He was, we later found out, subjected to a hate campaign – his car daubed with paint, hate mail through the door, obscene and threatening messages left on his answerphone. Rather than take early retirement from the force, he committed suicide.

Mo was considerably upset, but I suspect Corbett was even more gutted. Not because of Harry Ross's death – although that did leave a bad taste in everyone's mouths – but because the whole incident had put an end to his dreamed-of promotion; the one he had wanted so badly that he had forced a junior officer to take the flak for his misdemeanours. As a result of our investigation his promising career was all but over. He was now unlikely ever to rise above the rank of DI and Harry Ross's death meant that no one wanted to get too close to him any more – he had, after all, instigated that final hate campaign.

As I said before, Detective Inspector Dick Corbett was a dangerous bully. He had driven one man to his death, and who's to say he wouldn't like to take credit for a second one? After all, I had put an end to his life as top dog down at his local nick. He must really want me dead.

Suspect Dossier file No.:4
Subject: DETECTIVE INSPECTOR
WILL KENDRICK

Looking back into the past, thinking about all the people who might really want me dead, the one man I hope I'm not looking over my shoulder for is DI Will Kendrick. He was a Scouser, a decent family bloke and a good copper who did a good job, but my investigation into the Teddy Dicks affair left Kendrick's life in ruins. The whole business made him look more guilty and corrupt than the villain he had put away. After losing his job on the force, he lost his house – employment in Merseyside not being easily found by an ex-copper – and then his wife and kids, too. Sometimes I think there's no justice in this bloody world.

The background to this case was complicated. The South Lancashire Serious Crimes Squad was under internal investigation. They seemed adept neither at clearing up the crimes on their patch nor at investigating complaints against their own officers. It was probably no accident that my team was called in on this job. The Deputy Chief Constable in South Lancashire at the time was our former Deputy Assistant Commissioner, Trevor Dunning. We all knew him from the days when he was based in London. He was a big pal of Commander Huxtable – they had been in the army together and had known each other for thirty years – and I guess I had probably made an impression on him at some point. Although we had been surprised by his move away from the capital to become Deputy Chief Constable with the turnip-tops, it was just a calculated step towards his long-term goal – Commissioner of the Metropolitan Police.

They needed some fresh legs on the investigation team up north, so Harry, Mo and I set out for a few days in Liverpool. Our brief was to look into the case of two CID officers accused of fitting up an armed robber.

We spent the first night there in a hotel, drinking from the room's mini-bar and watching the news. As luck would have it, they televised a press conference with DAC John More, the man leading the investigation into the alleged corruption in the South Lancs Serious Crime Squad, and the man we were due to meet the following day. I remember very well that the televised conference was considerably livened up by one very gutsy journalist from the Liverpool press. Her name was Molly Cope; she was beautiful and she was giving the police panel a hard time. I made a mental note then that I had to interview her. I'd be very interested to hear Ms Cope's opinions of the South Lancs Serious Crimes Squad.

The next day the three of us converged on Huskisson Street Police Station, where the two coppers we had been sent to investigate were based. The events we were now examining had happened over eighteen months ago and probably would not have merited calling us in had not all this bad publicity hit the force when it did. However, we were there to pluck out all the rotten apples, so it was inevitable that the smallest molehill would turn into Mount Everest.

Eighteen months previously, DI Will Kendrick and DC James MacPhearson had arrested Edward ('Teddy') John Dicks for a string of armed robberies – four, to be precise – around the New Brighton and Wirral areas of Merseyside. They had obtained a taped confession but now Dicks's solicitor, in the light of the internal investigations, was screaming 'fit-up' and was hoping to take the case to the Court of Appeal. He maintained that his client had been stoned when arrested, so the confession was invalid, and had later been denied the presence of a solicitor when one was requested. Dicks himself was saying he was beaten into making the confession. Both Kendrick and MacPhearson denied the allegations, and so we were there to find out who was telling the truth – a known criminal with a drugs problem, or two experienced police officers. I would have hoped the answer was going to be an easy one; equally I had long since stopped being surprised at the rot and corruption that pervaded the ranks of Mr Peel's Finest.

We met DAC More in the Incident Room at Huskisson Street station. Already we had encountered huge hostility from the officers there, and John More wasn't planning to make us feel any more welcome. He told me we had two weeks to clear up the investigation into the Dicks case; we were to be thorough, but we must not turn the investigation into a witch-hunt. He also told me quite categorically that he supported Kendrick and MacPhearson, and Sergeant Poynton as well, the custody sergeant at Egberth Street who was also implicated in the investigation.

We started off by interviewing Teddy Dicks. Mo and I visited the cocky little bastard in prison. He told us that at 6 pm on the afternoon he was arrested he had been wandering around the streets, high as a kite and looking for a shag. That's when Kendrick arrested him, told him he was going to go down for all the armed robberies, and took him to Egberth Street nick, where he was beaten around a bit. The most interesting piece of information to come out of Dicks's story was the timing – it differed hugely from Kendrick's account, which stated that he said he didn't pick Dicks up until after 9 pm. Strange. It was something I'd have to look into. Mo and I then spoke with Dr Bedi, the station's police surgeon, who confirmed that when he had examined Dicks down in the cells the day after the arrest, his injuries were consistent with a one- to two-day old beating.

Meanwhile, Harry had gone down the pub – to speak with a 'witness' who said he had been with Dicks, fishing, at the time that one of the armed robberies of which Dicks had been accused was being committed. He also mentioned that Kendrick had always had it in for Dicks, and he remembered an occasion when Dicks had been drinking in the pub and Kendrick had walked in and promised Dicks he'd get him for the armed robberies. When Harry told me this, all I could think was: shit. It didn't help Kendrick's cause if it was general knowledge that he had a grudge against Dicks.

I thought it was about time I spoke with Molly Cope. Of course, being a left-wing journo she didn't want to talk to me, a copper in a suit, but I managed to persuade her to have breakfast with me the following day.

Unlike most of the women I knew, Molly looked fantastic in the morning, but I suspected she'd look good at any time of the day. It took a hell of a lot of will-power not to let my thoughts wander, to concentrate on getting two things out of her. In fact I wanted three, but decided the other could come later.

18   She told me it was her opinion that the South Lancashire squad was corrupt to the core

and that yes, she did have an informant who had an 'in' into the Dicks affair. But that was all she was giving me. I paid for breakfast, left the greasy spoon cafe she had chosen for our meeting, and went to join Harry down at Egberth Street nick, where we were due to interview Poynton, the custody sergeant on the desk the night Kendrick hauled in Dicks.

Poynton was very nervous. The interview was conducted in the presence of a Police Federation representative and it was over with pretty quickly. He told us that Dicks was stoned when he was brought in, and that Kendrick definitely signed him in at 10 pm, Dicks refusing the offer of a solicitor. That meant that when we compared the statements made to us by Dicks and the police officers, we had four unaccounted-for hours between 6 pm and the time when the police said Dicks was signed in. This was really pissing me off. Somebody was lying to us, and I was determined to get to the bottom of it.

Poynton finished his interview by telling us Kendrick was one of the best coppers around, while MacPhearson declined to be interviewed, sending me a written statement instead. This was getting extremely frustrating – all we were coming up with were handfuls of loose ends. But then Mo turned up something pretty useful. Down at Egberth Street nick she had discovered the notebook of one PC Alfreds, in which he had written that on the evening of Dicks's arrest, he had brought water and toilet paper to the prisoner in the cells at 8 pm. This put Dicks in the police station two hours earlier than Kendrick and the other officers were letting on.

I decided to talk to Molly Cope again – only this time she met me in the evening, over a drink. She admitted her informant had told her Dicks was picked up off the street at 6 pm – not 9 pm, as Kendrick maintained – and was taken to Egberth Street station, not Huskisson nick, which should have been the obvious choice as that's where Kendrick was based. Molly said the reason for this was because the custody sergeant at Egberth Street was a pal of Kendrick's, and would turn a blind eye to whatever happened in the cells. During the course of the night, Dicks had been beaten, intimidated and made to sign a confession, admitting having carried out the four hold-ups.

When she had finished her story I was left wondering how reliable her informant was. I was also wondering if she was wearing any underwear. Later that night I found out.

The following day Harry had the pleasure of interviewing PC Alfreds, an unremarkable young man with acne. He informed Harry that the information in his notebook was wrong – he'd written it down incorrectly, having always had a problem with the twenty four hour clock in that he regularly wrote down 10 o'clock as 20.00 hours instead of 22.00 hours. Harry and I both immediately thought that we had been wasting our time, but the interview had interesting repercussions.

Later on that day, I was attacked by a furious Molly Cope. She accused me of frightening off her informant, who was now refusing to speak to her. Her informant was PC Alfreds! I calmed her down, until even she could see the funny side and the enormous luck we had had in uncovering him. Maybe he wasn't such an unremarkable man after all. I decided to speak with him myself, to suggest a deal. I wanted him to tell me everything that had gone on at Egberth Street that evening, while in return I wouldn't tell anyone he was Molly Cope's informant. He talked. He told me that after the confession had been obtained from Dicks, a solicitor arrived at the station. He was another good friend of Kendrick's and advised Dicks to swallow the charges and do the time. PC Alfreds hinted at corruption all the way up in the South Lancs Police Force, which is why he had spoken to a journalist rather than to his superiors. The last thing he told me was that if I blew his cover he'd leave the force and never offer any more information – to me or anyone. By this stage I had totally reassessed my opinion of the 'unremarkable' PC Alfreds.

It was the wonderful Ms Cope who provided me with the final piece of information that decided me to speak with Kendrick off the record and alone. My previous conversations with him had not gone well. I had accused him of beating up Dicks, of denying him food and drink and a solicitor. His only response to me was that I should prove it. I now really wanted to speak with him, to get the truth out of him, which I knew he was keeping from me. Molly had uncovered another witness who said he saw Kendrick arresting Dicks in New Brighton between 5.30 pm and 6 pm. The witness was positive of the time as he was just shutting his shop for the night.

I met Kendrick in a pub which wasn't too far away from where he lived with his wife and kids. Nice neighbourhood, nice life. I couldn't believe he would jeopardise all of that to fit up a criminal who was in any case bound to be put away some day. I told Kendrick our meeting was off the record and that I had wanted to speak to him as the evidence was mounting against him, MacPhearson and Poynton. I listed all points not in his favour – Dicks's original complaint, the witness who had provided Dicks with a fishing alibi when Kendrick maintained he was holding up a post office, another witness who saw Kendrick arrest Dicks at 6 pm, and the fact that both the custody sergeant and the solicitor at Egberth Street Police Station were personal friends of Kendrick's. I then offered him a compromise: if he admitted to beating a confession out of Dicks, in return I wouldn't use the information in PC Alfred's notebook against him. MacPhearson and Poynton would walk while he would escape with a simple caution. Kendrick's reply was no deal. I had to admire the man. He seemed unshakeable.

By now we had been in Liverpool far too long. As predicted, the molehill had turned into a mountain and Harry, especially, was getting extremely pissed off with the whole thing. I had a vague feeling of unease about the entire case, but he exploded one evening and just pointed out the truth: that if Kendrick had played the game by the rules then Dicks wouldn't have been put away even though he was guilty of at least three of the hold-ups, while now everybody – us, the Police Complaints Authority, the DPP and Crown Prosecution Service – seemed to bending over backwards to get the little shit out of prison. Kendrick, a decent copper by all accounts, was being suffocated by the fall-out. My old argument of 'we're only doing our job' didn't sound very convincing, even to my ears.

We had done our job well. We had enough evidence on the Dicks case to warrant its being reopened. It sickened me to think Dicks might go free – my team had uncovered enough discrepancies and new evidence to invalidate the testimonies of Kendrick, MacPhearson and Poynton. I was surprised, therefore, when Kendrick rang me, requesting a meeting down by the docks. It was an uncomfortable meeting. He told me that the truth could always be hidden – or it could always be told. He knew about my affair with Molly Cope. He wasn't interested enough to tell anyone, to wreck any lives. He then told me the truth about the Dicks business. He had arrested him at 6 pm, but the man was so high that he just couldn't stop talking. So Kendrick brought him down to the docks and walked him around a bit to straighten him out before taking him to the police station. He never hit him

– he bought him a burger instead. He then took him down to Egberth Street nick and booked him in at 10 pm, to let him rest a bit once the after-effects of the Ecstasy he had taken had worn off. Kendrick had chosen Egberth Street nick rather than his own, Huskisson Street, because it was nearer the docks. He got Dicks a solicitor when he eventually asked for one the following day. He had also obtained a confession from a dangerous criminal. That was the truth.

I was glad to return to London, to some dull office paperwork and to my wife. She wasn't particularly interested in the investigation, which saved me having to drag my professional conscience over the coals again, and she didn't really want to know anything about what had gone on in Liverpool, which also suited me just fine. Molly Cope did ring me though – to tell me Kendrick had been suspended, pending the results of the CPS enquiry and possible prosecution by the DPP. Dicks had won his appeal, and walked free. I had done a good job.

Suspect Dossier file No.:5
Subjects: PC IAN HARTNELL &
COMMANDER PATRICK NEAME

I hate riots. They're frightening – really, genuinely frightening. People get hurt and in the mess quite often nobody is really sure who to blame for what, or even who started it all in the first place. Investigating the riot outside the Cringle Street factory resulted in the wrong person being hurt. Me. I was so wrapped up in my investigation, I was so involved with Molly Cope and Jenny Dean – my occasional light relief from Mulberry Street – and I was concentrating so hard on my personal vendetta against Commander Patrick Neame that I didn't see what was happening under my very nose. By the time I had got the final picture of what happened in the riot, by the time I had figured out who was to blame, by the time I had got sworn confessions and had gone home at the end of the day, I found I didn't have a wife. Sue had left me. And that's when the dark, violent times really started.

Before the investigations into the riot at Cringle Street, everything was coming up smelling of roses. I remember Sue and I were getting along just fine, and in the week that the riot broke had been invited to dinner with Commander Huxtable – Brian, as he was known to his friends – at his home. That seems like a lifetime ago. However, at the time I was getting on so well with him that when news of the riot came through, Brian wanted me to head the investigation. The information I had to hand was a bit unclear. A picket line was being policed outside a factory in Cringle Street. I can't even remember what was being produced there, but the bosses had decided the product had to be moved. The lorries had been loaded and were ready to leave the factory. The picket line was getting restless, feelings were beginning to run high, and so the police were ordered to disperse the crowd. The result was shown on TV. A full-scale riot ensued with barricades being pushed over, fighting breaking out between rioters and police, horses, journalists, shouting and screaming everywhere. Then something frightening happened – Molotov cocktails were thrown at the police and the TV cameras picked up one of our lads being burnt alive in his clothes, his mates rushing in to put him out. But my services weren't required to investigate that particular incident. I was told to find out which copper, during the course of the riot, had truncheoned one of the rioters over the head. He had used his truncheon to such good effect that the bloke was now lying in a coma at the London Royal Infirmary, with only a 50 per cent chance of ever coming out of it. His name was Billy Page, and his father, another factory worker down on the picket line, had that morning gone down to his local police station with his other son, Dan, and had lodged a formal complaint against the Tactical Support Group, the squad with the horses and riot gear, who were supposed to have been keeping the picket line in order.

So entered the troubleshooters – Mo, Harry and me. We went through the televised footage of the riot in my office, to see whether we had missed any clues. Re-watching the video I realised with a shock that I had missed something important. There, on the screen, in the thick of the riot, was Molly Cope. I knew she was in London these days, working for the *Guardian*, and it was a pleasant surprise to see her face again. I gave her a ring and she agreed to have dinner with me, and to supply me with newspaper pictures of the riot that we didn't have already. It seemed like a good enough excuse to both of us. Meanwhile, I thought the best place to start the investigation was to talk to Commander Patrick Neame, head of the TSG. I wanted all documentation, statements and video footage from the riot; anything, in fact, that would give us some sort of clue as to who the psychopath with the truncheon was. Harry and I visited Neame at Area HQ for an informal chat. What we were met with was a stone wall. We requested access to all documents. Neame informed us that in time we would get official reports from the officers involved in the riot. We were not to interview them beforehand as he believed his men were innocent until proved guilty. He wasn't going to give us the TSG video footage of the riot. In short, he was being an unhelpful, unco-operative bastard and I had no time for him. I told him I was demanding all documents on behalf of the Police Complaints Authority and I wanted him to give them to me. He had to agree. I knew I had won this particular round, but I could see how he despised me – because I had more political clout than him, and because he thought I was a shit. Still, I didn't care. I had got what I had come for. Almost. He informed me that they had no useful or enlightening video tapes of the riot, but that the best material was with the BBC. I prayed he wasn't stupid enough to send me out on a wild goose chase, but I'd find out soon enough.

I left Harry with Neame and went back to the office, where I made a phone call to the BBC. I arranged to meet the news editor the following day. Before going home that night I checked in with Mo. She had been down at the hospital, looking in on Billy Page. He was still in a coma and his chances were still 50/50. She had also made contact with Mrs Page, who was willing to talk to CIB. This was good news – her husband and son had refused to do so, thinking all coppers were bent bastards. Not an exceptionally inspired or original line of thought, but depressing nonetheless. I also learned that, ironically, the poor rookie who had been burnt by the Molotov cocktail was lying in a ward not too far away from Billy Page. PC Danny Dunn was about the same age, too.

The next day I arrived at the BBC, where I was met with great hostility from the news editor. This surprised me, as she had seemed quite willing to co-operate when I had spoken with her the day before. I wasn't so surprised, though, when I found out that Neame had beaten me to her that morning. He had been rude and heavy-handed and had threatened her with all sorts of injunctions if she used the film or released it to anyone. He had done a good job of spoiling my chances of getting any information from her. Round Two to him. I was so bloody livid I drove straight round to see him, demanding to see the tape. I knew they must already have a copy. I suggested he give it to Harry who, in the face of Neame's obstructiveness, was ploughing through all the documents connected with the riot. So far he had come up with nothing.

I went back to my office, only to be confronted by Deakin on the warpath, accompanied by Huxtable. He went on at me about my arrogant attitude to Neame. I couldn't believe it. Neame had rung up Deakin, told him I was a jumped-up little shit, and demanded I be dropped from the enquiry. And now Huxtable, too, was threatening to take me off the case. Unbelievable. I was just saying my piece about Neame and his obstructive, 23 unhelpful and downright rude attitude when Harry came in with the tape in hand. He was grinning. He put the tape in the machine and we all watched. The Cringle Street riot appeared in front of our eyes – the screaming, the horses charging, barriers going down – and Billy Page, scrambling over a wall, trying to escape the mayhem. Two policemen were running up to him and pulling him off the fence and ... and then Ed the Duck appeared on screen. The tape had been doctored. Neame had been tampering with the evidence. Huxtable left the office. The last thing he told me was that he was going to inform Neame that I was back on the case. Permanently.

Mo and I then left to interview the Page family. We parked our car outside the council house where they lived, which immediately fronted the street. No nice manicured front lawns in that area. Things began disastrously, even before we rang the doorbell. Two blokes walking down the street identified themselves as Billy's brother and a mate. They instantly recognised me as a copper and went for me. By the time Mrs Page had come to the door, Mo had Billy's brother in an armlock and I was nursing a split lip. Mrs Page soon sorted things out. She was obviously one of those women who ruled her men with a rod of iron. We all went inside the house for a cup of tea. Talking to Billy's brother and father, it seemed they were convinced that the copper who had truncheoned Billy was black. I could have killed Neame for tampering with that tape. Without it we had no way of knowing for sure who really was responsible.

That evening I dined with Molly at her flat. She gave me photos and a West Indian meal. She also wanted me to stay the night with her, to curl up in bed and watch a video. I couldn't. I wanted Sue. I had an overwhelming desire to be curled up in bed with my wife watching a film, something to take my mind off things. Molly showed me the video anyway. It was of the Cringle Street riot. God knows how she had obtained it – the woman was a marvel. We watched it all in complete silence. It was like re-experiencing a nightmare, but with one big difference . . . this time there was no unscheduled interruption from Ed The Duck. The two officers ran towards Billy, he was dragged off the fence, he went down, and then a flurry of confusing activity left one officer stooped over him before a medic arrived and the officer made off. I now knew we had a copper to question. No wonder Neame had been trying to keep this evidence from us.

The following day I showed the tape to Harry. Although it was not of the best quality, he identified the copper on the tape as one Colin Cameron, a West Indian. I told Neame to set up an identity parade, then got Billy's dad in to see whether he could make a positive identification. The men in the line-up all wore riot gear, as they had done on the night of the Cringle Street riot. To my surprise, they all had their visors down and, doubtless following Neame's instructions, they started to breathe heavily. Their visors misted up – Billy's dad could not make a positive ID. Neame was becoming a real pain in the arse. I wondered what it was with the man. I was sure he hated me even more than I hated him – and on a scale of 1 to 10, I was hovering around the twelve mark. Harry then came clean. He told me that in the days when he had been a sergeant in Special Branch, Neame was his Chief Super and the Super had been Deakin. Great. No wonder Deakin had been so eager to defend Neame. Harry also told me that Neame was gunning for me – he was loyal to his men and would protect them at all costs. I didn't care. I now had a suspect and I was going to interview him – even if he was one of Neame's boys, and even if Neame was accusing me of arrogance and racism.

Harry and I sat PC Colin Cameron down in the Interview Room and showed him the tape of the riot. I threatened him with suspension and arrest over the truncheoning – and then suggested he tell the truth. Harry and I had watched that video over and over again, and the truth was that Cameron hadn't truncheoned Billy Page. The video camera never lied. What it showed was Cameron restraining an unidentified police officer from beating Billy Page, and then calling for help when his TSG colleague ran off. Any fool could see that Cameron knew who the officer responsible for the truncheoning was, but he wasn't talking. He wasn't going to grass on a mate. I tried hard. I told him his career would be over if he didn't cough. He told me it was probably over whichever way he looked at it; if he grassed on his mate then he'd be ostracised by his colleagues; if he didn't, then I would stitch him up. I then remembered where I had seen Cameron before – that is, before he had been positively identified on the videotape. I had seen him at the London Royal Infirmary. As he was obviously not a friend of Billy's, then he must be a friend of the injured copper, Danny Dunn. Everything was slowly falling into place. Off the record, I asked Cameron whether the attack on Billy Page was in retaliation for the torching of PC Dunn. Cameron could only nod. Page wasn't guilty of the Molotov attack, but he had paid the price of being on the other side when the battle had begun. See what I mean about riots? Everybody stands a chance of getting hurt – especially the innocent.

I went with Cameron to the hospital, ostensibly to visit Dunn, but on the way we stopped off at Billy Page's room. We peered in through the glass in the door. He was still on a life-support machine, and as ever, his family were with him. As Cameron took in the tragic scene at Billy's bedside, I could feel him starting to seethe with rage. The bastard who had clubbed young Billy had plenty to answer for. Not only had he destroyed the life of a fine young man, he had brought anguish and grief to the Page family and dumped Colin Cameron, supposedly his friend, deep in the shit. Cameron's loyalty to his so-called mate was collapsing faster than the Berlin Wall. When we went to see Danny Dunn, Cameron asked me to wait outside. After a hushed conversation with Dunn, I was called in. Cameron looked me straight in the eye and slowly nodded. He had just made the toughest decision of his life.

The maniac responsible for the truncheoning was PC Ian Hartnell – a cocky, hot-headed little bastard who didn't deserve protection from Neame, from Cameron, or from anyone else. He could hardly argue in the face of the video evidence, so we did him. I personally wanted to do Neame as well. It was my intention to have him for obstruction of justice and tampering with police evidence, but he was protected by powerful friends. He hated me then and probably does so even more now, because over the past couple of years I've been chipping away at his protective layer, getting rid of a few of those powerful colleagues who had been watching his back. Maybe he could be striking a blow for them now. Maybe he knows he has to get me first, before I get him. I can't afford to rule him out. Neither should I rule out the young thug, Hartnell. He's certainly crazy enough to want to start putting the frighteners on me, but he's more likely to blame Cameron and he's not in the same league as Neame. Neame would come to my funeral and spit on my grave.

Suspect Dossier file No.: 6
Subject: CHIEF INSPECTOR
IAN STUBBS

The summer my wife left me was glorious. It was hot and sultry, and I was running around everywhere, trying not to think about the mess my personal life was in. Sue had left – ironically, on a misunderstanding. She had followed me in the car one lunchtime, convinced I was still seeing Jenny Dean. She saw me having lunch with her and assumed she was still my hot item. She couldn't have been more wrong. I was having lunch with Jenny to tell her we were through, but that I still wanted us to be friends. What a cliché – and like most clichés, it was a load of old bollocks. Sue left, so I ran straight back into the arms of WPC Dean. After all, I had nowhere else to go. And because I didn't want to think about my home life much I really threw myself into my job. If I had been working hard before then I was in overdrive now. Because I felt like a cheating, lying, cruel bastard I determined to rid the force of all other cheating, lying, cruel bastards. Unfortunately, I didn't have a 100 per cent success rate.

The whole Markham affair certainly brought that home to me. We were investigating DS Chris Markham of Oakwood Police Station on the basis of an official complaint by George Tolly, a criminal who was in prison awaiting trial. He had been nicked by Markham, but was willing to make a deal, saying he could prove Markham was receiving corrupt payments from other criminals and was in effect running his own protection racket. He also said that the only reason he was in prison was because he had refused to pay Markham any more cash – so Markham had him up on trumped-up charges.

That's why, one beautiful Saturday morning, I found myself sitting in Battersea Park with Harry, drinking cappuccino and watching two blokes chatting on a bench. Mo was on the grass a few yards away, playing at being boyfriend/girlfriend with DS Gerry Caplan. Ironic in the light of later revelations, really. Mo would probably have given a more convincing performance with a WPC.

Anyway, they were staking out the two blokes on the bench as well. From our positions we noticed a brown envelope change hands, and that's when we made our move. Mo and Gerry approached one of the men, who had left the bench and was making towards the park exit. They identified themselves – and with an impressive show of kick boxing, the bloke winded both of them and did a runner. Harry and I approached the other bloke, who was still sitting on the bench. Sergeant Chris Markham. I accused him of receiving a £1,000 corrupt payment. He paled. This was his career on the line. I told him he was being investigated and his game was up; Harry took the envelope. Markham told us it was full of false MOT certificates and that David Panter – our kick-boxing friend – was a known police informant. Harry opened the envelope, and just for a moment it looked like Markham was telling the truth – until Harry uncovered a left luggage chit in amongst all the other crap in the envelope. Markham started to babble, saying he was set up. We invited him to come to Victoria Station with us, to see what that left-luggage chit would produce.

At Victoria we found what we expected: £1,000 in used notes, stuffed into an old sports bag. All the time Markham was declaring his innocence. Well, he would say that, wouldn't he? We arrested him there, and Harry and I took him back to CIB headquarters for interviewing. As expected, we didn't get much out of him other than denials of the corruption of which he was accused.

Deakin decided to interfere, as usual, telling me the luggage chit was a pretty weak piece of incriminating evidence, but I didn't care. I especially didn't care because my own life was in deep shit. I was going to throw the book at Markham to teach him a bloody good lesson – that he didn't mess with the CIB, and he especially didn't cross Tony Clark. Already, I'd had enough of Sergeant Markham and Oakwood Police Station. I reminded Deakin that Markham was the fifth officer out of Oakwood who'd been caught out – in the past, accusations had included the planting of evidence, receiving stolen goods and improper association. The overtime rates at Oakwood were the highest in the Met, and I decided I was going to put a stop to all these abuses. I told Deakin I was going to throw a net over Oakwood and round up all those bastards who were extorting money and fitting up petty criminals for crimes they hadn't committed. I was going to scrub the Met clean – and I knew I had Huxtable's blessing. If I was 100 per cent correct. At the time, I didn't have any doubts.

The following day Harry, Mo and I, together with other back-up officers, descended on Oakwood. Within seconds the police station was humming with the news that the 'Rubber Heels' had arrived. I told everyone to stop working, clear the office and wait in the canteen until we told them they could go home. The nick was in effect closed down, and I informed Chief Super Horsforth that CIB was going to go through all of Oakwood's records. We wanted duty logs, vehicle logs, message books and informants' files. I could tell that everyone at the nick was outraged, but there was nothing they could do. I was in charge. My men then sat down at the deserted desks and started to go through the files. I prayed to God we'd come up with more than just a load of paper. I knew my balls were on the line over this.

The investigation was going to take some time – weeks maybe – but I tried to stop in every day, to keep in touch with how the work was going. Mo discovered that Markham's partner, a DC Taylor, had claimed expenses for an excessive amount of mileage. It was pathetic. Small beer. If that was the best we could do then we were in trouble. It was during one of those check-ups that I first spoke with Chief Inspector Ian Stubbs. He looked like a regular salt-of-the-earth sort of bloke, with his greying moustache and a face which carried an expression of wry humour. In fact he looked a bit like Jimmy Greaves. His genial appearance, however, masked a dangerous and ambitious character. This was an officer willing to shaft his own boys in order to save his own neck. He was despicable – amoral, and capable of any amount of viciousness. I actually trusted him at first, but now I know he would easily get rid of me if he thought I could touch him. And maybe he's trying. I don't know.

My first meeting with Stubbs was on the stairs at Oakwood nick. I'd heard his name being mentioned earlier in the canteen, and knew he was popular with the other officers. I asked him about Markham and remember being told, 'You hang around with dogs, you get fleas.' He went on to tell me I wouldn't win any wings on that case. It was then that I thought he was a bastard. Meanwhile, investigations of Oakwood's records weren't turning up any more incriminating information. The best Harry could come up with was that the 27 officers did a lot of 'pubbing and clubbing' with various criminals and informants, claiming expenses for those meetings. Hardly an offence for which to shut down a police station. And I had heard that the Police Federation had lodged a formal complaint on behalf of Oakwood with the Home Secretary. I was beginning to get slightly worried that this case wasn't going the way I had hoped it would go. It was time I interviewed Markham again.

Harry and I brought Markham in to the CIB offices for questioning. He told us the meeting in the park had been set up by David Panter, to pass on some stolen MOTs. He denied setting up the meeting in order to accept money from Tolly, and went on to say that since he nicked the man it was obvious that Tolly would have a grudge against him – hence the accusations. I wasn't having any of that. I drew attention to his bank account. We had uncovered that over the past three years a sum of £18,000 had been paid at regular intervals into his personal account. Markham stayed silent. I then asked him about an unauthorised check on one Anthony Prentice that he had run through the National Police Computer. Markham's answer was that he was trying to trace Prentice for a friend, whose sister got pregnant by Prentice. I didn't believe a word he said. It was time to speak to Panter.

It was easy enough to find Panter – there aren't too many kick boxing centres in South London. Harry and I pulled him in for questioning. We accused him of conspiracy to corrupt a police officer, which carries a heavy sentence. Unruffled, Panter maintained he was nothing more than a go-between; he had done the same deal before with Markham, three weeks prior to the one at which we were present. He also told us the left luggage tickets were Markham's idea.

I sent Mo off to the left luggage counter at Victoria Station, while I paid an informal visit to Chief Inspector Ian Stubbs, to chat to him about Markham and what he was really like. Stubb's summing-up wasn't calculated to please me. He thought Markham was a bit like me – ambitious, and 'very Cecil Gee-ish'. Not terribly flattering. Mo had had a bit more success down at Victoria, however. She had found the stub of another deposit tag made out by Markham – three weeks before the one we had collected. So Panter's story seemed to be standing up. While she was there she had also chatted up the bloke in charge of left luggage, who had told her everything she had ever wanted to know about the left luggage office and how it worked. When she asked about the security cameras there she was informed the tapes were kept running twenty-four hours a day, but only stored for a week before they were deleted. That was a pity. We could have done with video footage of Markham picking up the bag on the first occasion.

A couple of days later I was bollocked by Deakin again. This time he waved a copy of Police Review in my face and asked me what I was going to do about it. I felt my bowels contract when I read the article that had caused all the upset. A journalist had interviewed Chief Inspector Ian Stubbs, who had in a very roundabout way alluded to our heavy-handedness at Oakwood Police Station. Deakin accused me of a piss-poor performance, telling me I was really in the shit, and finally suggested that I visit George Tolly, who was on remand at Wormwood Scrubs, just to make sure his story was solid. So I went.

Tolly was an unpleasant, whining little man. He told me he had been fitted up by Markham, who had planted a sawn-off shotgun in the back of his car and then told him in the nick that if Tolly didn't pay up he'd work in another two robberies to tie in with his trial. Markham had now received two payments from him. I believed Tolly. I went back to the office in a filthy temper, only to be intercepted by Harry, who told me that Markham had approached him on his day off and had informed him that the £18,000 in his bank account had been deposited there by his father-in-law as some sort of tax fiddle. I was furious. I told Harry he should enter that informal meeting in the incident book. I didn't care that he and Markham had once been friendly – apparently they had been on the same police shooting team. I was in so much shit already I didn't want members of my staff to be caught by Deakin, or anyone else, associating with officers under investigation. It was then that Harry gave me a strange look and said I should take an example from out of my own book. I knew he meant Jenny.

Now there was a person whose life was in as big a mess as mine. Not only was she putting me up, she was also somehow loosely involved in a case which was being investigated by other officers in CIB. Being Jenny, she was worried sick about it, even though I had told her it wasn't important. I made a mental note to be nice to her that evening and take her out to dinner.

I then went over and checked up on Mo. She was buried under a pile of videos – it seemed she had made quite an impression on the man in left luggage, who had sent all the tapes to her. Apparently in the week of Markham's first pick-up there had been a bomb scare at the station, and all the tapes had been taken by the bomb squad. They had then been returned to British Rail and the left luggage officer had sent them on to Mo, hoping they'd be of some help. They were. She didn't find Markham anywhere on the videos, but she found Panter – twice. In order to make the accusations against Markham stick, Panter and the people he was working with had to prove that Markham had received one previous payment, three weeks before we caught him. So it was Panter we saw on video putting the bag in, and then taking it out again in the name of Markham. All this time Markham had been telling the truth. I had been in shit plenty of times in the past, but I'd never been is in as deep as this. This time I was in up to my neck, if not over my head. I braced myself and went in to see Deakin.

He was furious. Purple with rage. As far as he was concerned the whole case had gone belly-up and there now was a danger that the Crown Prosecution Service would pull Markham from giving evidence at Tolly's trial, since Markham was incapable of giving impartial evidence. Without that evidence, Tolly would walk. Deakin wasn't interested in the fact that I thought there was more to this case than finding Markham innocent. I thought somebody at Oakwood was pulling strings; certainly something very suspicious was going on, and I was going to find out what it was, even if it killed me and even if I had to do it whilst looking for another job. My performance over the past few weeks had been pretty poor and I reckoned my job was on the line. Living with Jenny wasn't helping my cause, either, but I couldn't give her up. Not at that point in my life, anyway.

My stand changed dramatically, however, after a quiet little chat with Harry in the pub. He'd been talking to another CIB mate who was working on the Carswell inquiry, the inquiry in which Jenny appeared to have had some incidental involvement. Or at least, that's what I had been led to believe. It seemed that WPC Jennifer Dean was going to be served with a 163 the following morning, informing her that she was under investigation over an alleged conspiracy to pervert the course of justice. If I was found to be living with her when the notice was served I knew I could kiss my job goodbye. Harry and I shot over to her flat and he waited as I cleared out all my stuff. Jenny was there, but I couldn't tell her anything. I felt like a shit, but just recently I had been getting quite used to that feeling. I cleared out of her flat and, I hoped, out of her life for good. Had that happened, things might have been very different today. Sadly, even our best intentions don't always work out as planned.

The next day, probably while Jenny was being served with her 163, I was back in the office to interview Panter again. I told him that he'd been caught on videotape, and asked him whether he had been doing Tolly a favour. Panter told me Markham was clean. Tolly was nicked good and proper but the complaint against Markham wasn't revenge. It was because Tolly felt he hadn't been looked after well enough by his friends – especially by one in particular. One Chief Inspector Ian Stubbs out of Oakwood nick. Panter then told me the whole story. Stubbs had been on a retainer from Tolly for years – until Markham blundered in and got Tolly for the shotgun. Stubbs then organised the whole set-up to make sure that Tolly would walk at trial when Markham's evidence was kicked out of court. Panter told me that was how Stubbs ran Oakwood Police Station, and everyone in it as well. By the sound of things, Markham was the only decent copper in that nick. The reason Panter himself was involved was because Stubbs had made him an offer he couldn't refuse.

Panter's confession had landed a real hot potato in my lap. I went over to interview Stubbs at home. He greeted me with a bottle of Chablis and a denial of everything Panter had said. He told me Panter was a slag while George Tolly was a good grass who deserved protection. I asked whether that stretched to accepting payment for protection. I reckoned that while in the nick Tolly threatened to blow the whistle on Stubbs's little game, which was why Stubbs had set up Markham in order to get Tolly off. Again, Stubbs wasn't commenting. He thought he was sitting pretty, but I knew that with just a touch more digging, I could bury the little creep.

I went back to CIB headquarters and explained the entire situation to Deakin. He then went to Huxtable with my story. The result wasn't what I expected.

Between them, my two bosses decided to put Stubbs on a back burner – to save him for a rainy day. They were unsure whether Panter's evidence would put Stubbs away – it was unlikely Tolly would verify Panter's story as he had his own back to protect – and for the moment, because of my inept bungling in closing down Oakwood station, CIB had egg on its face. Huxtable and Deakin decided that Markham would be disciplined for the unauthorised computer check he had carried out, while the official line to the press would be that the thorough investigation at Oakwood should serve as an 'example to other police stations of CIB's vigour in rooting out corruption at all levels in the police force'.

So Stubbs was going to be saved for later, and as far as I know he's still simmering away on that back burner. He knows I've got something on him – enough, perhaps, to put him away. And as I've said before, he's an amoral, corrupt bastard with a taste for Chablis and for manipulating people. He has good cause to want to manipulate me out of the way altogether.

The whole Markham business ended much as it had begun – with a hysterical woman accusing me of cheating on her. Only Jenny wasn't going to walk quietly out of my life, like Sue did. Jenny rang me in the office to inform me that if she was going down, then I was going down with her. I had to see her again for all the wrong reasons. We both needed each other – probably more than ever – but equally we were both disastrous for each other. For the first time in my life I felt well and truly trapped.

Suspect Dossier file No: 7
Subject: CHIEF SUPERINTENDENT CHARLIE McGREGOR

When Jenny and I got back together after she had been served with the 163, I think I suspected that I was instigating the beginning of the end of my career. Looking back, I realise now how many enemies I had made and how many friends I had lost. I was no longer the rising star in the department – the laurels had passed to a public school golden boy, Detective Superintendent David Graves.

Huxtable had stopped inviting me to soirées at his place – no doubt he was embarrassed that my perfectly suitable wife had left me because I couldn't keep my hands off a WPC who was under CIB investigation. And by this stage I just didn't know what was happening any more. My Midas touch was working in reverse – everything I got my hands on turned to shit.

With all of this preying on my mind, I welcomed the assignment to investigate a division of the drugs squad, an investigation which I was to run jointly with Thames Customs and Excise. Seemed to me like it would be a bit of a change, maybe even a rest, a chance to mess around on boats. As ever, it was naive optimism on my part. By the end of this investigation I would lose even more friends, forfeit Deakin's support for good, and discover that the woman with whom I was living hadn't been telling me the truth about her love life and was now in deep trouble – so much so that her problems made my uncomfortable predicament seem like a stroll in the park.

It was Huxtable who filled me in on the Customs and Excise investigation. He was irritated that I was late into the office that morning (I'd had a terrible row the night before with Jen and had subsequently overslept), but he told me to get in the car and he'd explain everything on the way to Customs and Excise headquarters. It seemed that the previous evening Steve Fisher, a Customs and Excise officer, had gone missing whilst on observation. He was part of a team which had been staking out a yacht down at St Katherine's Dock. The team had been observing a party given by Harry Chandler – a man they knew was dealing in drugs imported from Rotterdam. The goods were coming into the country via Old Father Thames and the Port of London. The Excise men wanted to net Chandler and his whole web of contacts, starting with the three ringleaders, Hendricks (the Dutch connection), Karunadasa (an Asian 'businessman') and Chandler himself. The stake-out team had positively identified their three main suspects on board during the party and that's when Steve Fisher, in frogman's gear, was sent out to the yacht, to get a closer view of the activities and possibly fire off some snapshots. It was then that the observation team, monitoring the yacht from dry land, noticed that Chandler's bodyguards had melted away from the party and were nowhere to be seen. The Excise men were in radio contact with Fisher and warned him to get out of there, but received no response. Four hours later he had still not reported back to the observation team. That's when they realised something had gone wrong and Ryman, the officer in charge of the stake-out, rang his guvnor to tell him of Fisher's disappearance.

That's how I came to be heading for Customs and Excise HQ with Huxtable. Exactly why CIB's presence was required wasn't clear, but we were due for a full debriefing about the case. The implication from Huxtable was that we might not like what we had heard once we were had learnt all the details.

When we arrived, we were introduced to various members of the stake-out team including Jim Ryman and his guvnor, Chief Inspector Hughes. We then looked at some photographs which had been taken during the previous night's observation both prior to and after Fisher's disappearance. The slides were in chronological order – they showed that at 12.30 am Karunadasa was the last man to arrive at the party. Fisher made radio contact for the final time at 00.35 am. Between 2.30 and 3 am the party broke up. And at 4 am Chandler headed out on a small boat up the river, where he was intercepted by a Thames Division police launch. Both boats then moved upstream, out of sight of the camera. A few minutes later the boats reappeared and went their separate ways – one upstream, one downstream.

It was at this point that we found out why CIB had been invited to join the debriefing. Customs and Excise had it on good authority that senior officers from the Met – the Drugs and Immigration Divisions – were somehow involved with Chandler and his set-up. The reason why Customs and Excise didn't ask for help from the Drugs Squad was because they suspected that officers from it and from Thames Division were working for the opposition. Huxtable told Hughes that vague suspicions weren't sufficient grounds for an investigation. He wanted hard evidence. Hughes then handed him a pile of documents. And that's when I knew we were in trouble.

All the Customs and Excise evidence, what there was of it, pointed to the involvement of the Drugs Squad led by Charlie McGregor. And Charlie McGregor was everybody's friend and favourite, due for early retirement within a couple of weeks. Indeed, I remembered that Deakin and Huxtable had gone to his retirement party a couple of days before these revelations. There had been speculation amongst the senior officers that McGregor was seeking early retirement because he had been overtaken by Dick Sharpe as head of the Drugs Squad, but McGregor denied that rumour, saying it was simply that he wanted the easy life in Spain. I couldn't say I blamed him. In fact I envied the bastard. And now this. If the Customs and Excise accusations were true, then a lot of senior police officers would be extremely embarrassed, politically. In fact, Huxtable decided to go to Deputy Assistant Commissioner Dunning over this one, and was advised that McGregor had to be investigated. Because of the sensitive nature of that investigation, however, Huxtable told me that my team's enquiries had to be carried out in secret.

Nobody was to know who we were investigating – not even Deakin. It was then that I remembered that Deakin was a good friend of McGregor's. In fact, since McGregor was such good friends with nearly every senior police officer, if even a whiff of our investigation got out he was sure to be tipped off by someone. Once a pro like him started covering his tracks we wouldn't pick up as much as a toeprint.

Next day I informed Mo and Harry we were assigned to Customs and Excise, and warned them of the secrecy that had to cloak our investigation. I told them in a nutshell what we were investigating. Customs Officer Steve Fisher had gone missing, his colleagues at Customs and Excise were alleging that he'd been murdered, and that the villains responsible had had the help of the police officers on the Thames Division launch in disposing of the body. The villains had access to the launch through their connections with Charlie McGregor and his drugs squad. Then we got down to business.

We first spoke with Ryman, the leader of the party that had staked out Chandler's yacht. He informed us that previous random searches on chartered yachts in the Thames had uncovered several stashes of drugs – cocaine, mainly. When the results of the random searches over several months were reviewed there was one name that cropped up a little too often for it to be a coincidence – Albatross Charter. It seemed that Albatross's clients took their recreational sailing a little less seriously than their recreational narcotics. And Harry Chandler owned 51 per cent of Albatross's shares.

Another uncomfortable coincidence turned up when we discovered that one of Chandler's yachts had been used the previous summer for a pleasure cruise for disabled children. The outing had been organised by a Thames Division officer. Ryman seemed to think that this was conclusive evidence that Chandler and McGregor were somehow connected. I thought it was a bit tenuous, but Harry was rather more vocal about it. It was obvious that his comments got right up the nose of Ryman's junior, a hothead called David Ray. Ryman and I had practically to pull Ray away from Harry's throat. Things were already looking pretty frosty on the liaison front at Customs and Excise, and we hadn't even begun. The atmosphere in that office was thick with dislike and resentment – it was plain that the only reason we were sitting there, talking with Ryman and his lot was because the latter's boss, Chief Inspector Hughes, had demanded a degree of co-operation. The final piece of information Ryman gave us was that his men had found out the names of the two officers who had been on the Thames launch on the night of the party. I made a mental note to talk to Sergeant Carr and Inspector Anderson. It was Anderson, after all, who had organised the disabled kids' party on Chandler's yacht.

The following day I left Harry with David Ray down at Customs and Excise HQ (I didn't see why I should be the only one having a hard time) while Ryman and I visited the morgue. A body had been washed up on the banks of the Thames, downriver from St Katherine's Dock. Ryman identified it as Steve Fisher. He told me Fisher had been his best mate, and then asked me a for a big favour. He wanted me to keep my mouth shut about the identification. I couldn't believe that he was asking me to do that. This was now a murder enquiry, and if we delayed calling in the murder squad, they would throw the book at us. Every minute we held back, vital forensic evidence might be lost or destroyed and their chances of nailing the murderer would become that much slimmer. Ryman argued that if anyone else in the Met got involved, word would filter back to McGregor and from him to Chandler, spoiling my chances of taking McGregor and, more importantly, his chances of shutting down the drugs network. Fisher and he had been working on this case for months and, Ryman said, if we blew it now, Fisher's death would have been for nothing. There was a good chance that the slags who snuffed Fisher had not identified him as being from Customs and Excise. Ryman reckoned that Chandler and his mates were committed to bringing in a major shipment within the next few days and that they were arrogant enough to try to pull it off still, despite the incident with Fisher. Against my better judgement, I agreed to hold off calling in the murder squad. Ryman deserved the chance to avenge the death of his friend, and I didn't really want to lose McGregor now that we had got this far.

Mo, meanwhile, had been sent out with a Home Office Immigration official who was also working with Customs and Excise. Illegal immigrants can often provide a lead on drugs traffickers, both trades being smuggling operations, and this was where the smooth and extravagant Mr Karunadasa came in. Mo later told me all about her afternoon with Zenab, the Home Office official. She was obviously shocked, and she doesn't normally shock that easily. The two women had visited an immigrant in a hostel, showing her photographs of Chandler and his partners. Zenab told Mo that the woman they had been talking to, Shisheeta, was working in a sweatshop in Brick Lane, fourteen hours a day for £1 per hour. She had come in to Britain illegally from Holland on one of Chandler's boats.

Shisheeta and her family – her husband and three children – all worked for Karunadasa's people. They provided cheap labour, while in return they were exploited over their accommodation and blackmailed over their illegal status. It was appalling, and criminal, but I had to remind Mo that, even if we collected watertight evidence, there was nothing she could do. Our job was to investigate police officers and deal with complaints. It was someone else's job to put a stop to the exploitation of illegal immigrants. We had enough on our plate doing our own job without interfering in someone else's.

Mo, Harry and I met up later at CIB offices with our various findings – the atmosphere was much calmer there than at Customs and Excise. Pooling all of our information, we came up with what we thought was Chandler's set-up. His partner, Hendricks, would process the drugs through Rotterdam. Karunadasa and Chandler bankrolled the entire operation and, if Ryman and his team were correct, the Met was turning a blind eye to the chartered yachts which were bringing the drugs in from Rotterdam because Charlie McGregor was in Chandler's pay. Customs and Excise only stumbled in on the act by chance through random checks they had carried out on Albatross-chartered vessels. It was also possible that the illegal immigrants brought in on Chandler's yachts were being used as mules, physically carrying the drugs across international borders to save any of Chandler's men from having to get their hands dirty. I was itching to question Anderson and Carr of the Thames Division, but I couldn't afford to alert them to the fact that CIB were on to them. That would ruin Ryman's planned drugs bust on Chandler. I told Harry to stake them out instead.

As I was leaving the building that night to get back to yet another disastrous evening with Jenny, I was stopped by Deakin, who demanded to know what was going on. I feigned utter stupidity and he warned me not to take the piss. I felt bad not telling him, because Deakin was actually a pretty fair boss. What really lifted him in my estimation, however, was that he despised Golden Boy David Graves even more than he hated me.

The following day I went to Huxtable with my findings. I showed him the list of documents which detailed the number of contacts between McGregor and Chandler, Karunadasa and Anderson over the past six months. As I expected, Huxtable thought it too circumstantial to build up a case against McGregor. What we needed were confessions, or to catch McGregor with money or cocaine in his briefcase – preferably both. I had to go back to Customs and Excise and try to tie in more closely with Ryman's people.

I reached their offices and immediately entered into a huge row with Ryman. He accused me of trying to scupper his operation by asking for details from Fisher's post-mortem. Ryman was paranoically convinced that any enquiries into Fisher's death would alert McGregor. I was just in the mood to go nose-to-nose with him. Did he think I was an idiot? Hadn't I promised to keep the murder squad at bay until he'd finished his business? I felt like punching his lights out, but settled for telling him that I'd called in a favour from a friend to get hold of the details and that my source was leakproof. The forensic results showed that Fisher had been dead before he hit the water and was then almost certainly moved downstream where an attempt was made to weight the body. Ryman started to cool down a bit, and at that point Ray rushed in to tell us that Chandler and Karunadasa had met up with Hendricks.

Intelligence from the Dutch police led us to believe that Hendricks had received a massive delivery of cocaine in Amsterdam, and we knew that Chandler had two boats ready and waiting in Rotterdam. At least one of the yachts was scheduled to return to London the following day. The Customs and Excise drugs bust was now on.

Harry and I were in on the raid with Ryman, Ray and the whole team. I thought both of us had a right to be there, since we had become so involved in the case. Harry's observation of Carr and Anderson had paid off to a degree – earlier on in the day he had followed them to an out-of-the-way warehouse where they had met up with Charlie McGregor – frustratingly, however, he couldn't hear what had been said. The fact that they had arranged such a clandestine rendezvous at this particular time, though, was highly suspicious. McGregor was either warning the Thames Division men that the shipment was coming in, or he had got wind of the bust and was warning them off.

As it transpired, the latter may well have been true. The whole bust turned into a fiasco. It seemed that Chandler – just for this trip – had changed his *modus operandi*. Instead of a yacht bringing in the cocaine, which was what usually happened, the cargo had been diverted somewhere else. The yacht which was under observation turned out to be a decoy. It was clean. Customs and Excise had blown their bust, and had fallen flat on their faces. Of course, they blamed CIB for leaking information, but it hadn't been us. It was probably a simple case of Charlie McGregor and Harry Chandler realising that Customs and Excise were on to their little game and changing their routine at the last minute. I felt sorry for Ryman especially, but now it was my turn to take over and I had Charlie McGregor in my sights.

I had heard that, down at CIB, when Huxtable had told Deakin what I had been working on, Deakin had been speechless. He had agreed, however, to be prepared to swoop on McGregor's men on the given command. It must have been very hard for him; some of them were his best mates. He knew Anderson from the Thames Division – and Anderson was right in it. Forensic evidence had placed Fisher's body in the Thames Division launch before it had been dumped downstream. There was no way out – Anderson was ready to talk to Harry and me. Maybe he had got sick of all the killings, extortion and misery that Chandler and McGregor had involved him in over the years, or maybe he was just trying to save his own skin. Either way, he told us all we wanted to know about Charlie McGregor and his set-up with Chandler.

Although the Customs and Excise drugs bust had found Chandler clean, he was arrested a couple of days later when a container ship carrying cargo for him reached

London. The container was packed with illegal immigrants, all of whom had paid their life savings for the privilege, and all of whom had been forced to swallow condoms full of cocaine before they embarked on their luxury cruise from Rotterdam. One condom had burst inside the stomach of an Asian youth, and he had died. The remaining immigrants locked in the container had then made such a noise when the ship docked in London that the Port Authority had been alerted, and so the whole sordid story came to light.

More frustrating was the fact that McGregor got away. Someone – possibly Deakin – must have given him the nod about our investigations, and he had slipped off quietly to Spain. At least, that's where I assume he's holed up. He must keep a pretty low profile on the Costas as no one that I know has ever heard from him and nobody has seen him since the day of the aborted drugs bust. It would seem that he vanished into thin air, his police pension still unclaimed. Obviously crime pays better than a Chief Super's pension. However, I've made it impossible for him to return to the UK where all his friends and family are – although these days a few of his friends are behind bars. Charlie McGregor mixed with some pretty hard and ruthless characters. He could be trying to get back at me now – it would be easy enough for him to pay someone to do me in. But somehow these death threats seem a little too slow for somebody with the contacts Charlie has. On the other hand, he may be relaxing in the sun by his swimming pool, enjoying the thought that I'm skulking around London waiting for my number to be called. If that's what he thinks then he's got it all wrong – I won't let this whole mess affect my entire life, but then again, I can't afford simply to ignore a death threat from a man like Charlie McGregor.

Suspect Dossier file No.:8
Subject: DETECTIVE INSPECTOR GORDON

I mention Detective Inspector Gordon in connection with my current situation because the man was a nasty piece of work who loved to kick people when they were down. He hated me – he thought my attitude towards criminals was too liberal. He was a natural bully whose solution to most problems was to kick the shit out of the nearest available person. Maybe he is the one sending me these threatening letters – he'd love to see me sweat.

I had the misfortune to come into contact with DI Gordon because of a suicide in the cells at St Helen's Police Station – Gordon's home nick. A PC Stan Fulford had been doing the rounds at the nick and had found that one of the recent lock-ups, a young black man, had hanged himself in his cell.

I remember being called out in the middle of the night to get to St Helen's. I remember this especially because at the time I was sleeping in my own flat. I wasn't staying with Jenny – I'd just found out that she had been shagging DS Eddie Hargreaves. He was the sergeant involved in the Carswell enquiry, the enquiry through which Jenny had been served her 163 – the form notifying her that she was under investigation. I went crazy. I didn't like the thought that she was sleeping with anyone other than me, and I especially hated it that her other bedfellow was Eddie Hargreaves. I couldn't believe she would be so stupid – she was in trouble up to her neck, but for some strange reason that didn't seem to be far enough for her. I told her that she was going the right way about making sure that she got herself in way over her head. This, of course, made her cry, and I just couldn't take any more. I also needed a good night's sleep, so I went back to my flat, where my good night's sleep was interrupted at 2.30 am by the phone ringing. No rest for the wicked, obviously.

When I reached St Helen's Police Station I found the police surgeon, Dr Owen Smith, already there, examining the body. The boy had hanged himself with a tie. This in itself was bad – the custody sergeant should have taken it away from him before the lad was locked in the cells, but other than that, there were no suspicious marks on the body and no signs that a struggle had taken place in the cells. So far the case was looking like a straightforward suicide – if a suicide can ever be described as straightforward. I still rang Harry and Mo and asked them to join me. I didn't see why I should be the only poor bastard deprived of sleep.

While I waited for them to turn up I was greeted by Chief Superintendent Lyon, the Divisional Commander, and Inspector Rooney. Rooney filled me in on the dead lad's background. His name was Joseph Pierce and he was eighteen years old. He had been brought in together with his friend, Dilly, for possession of drugs. Pierce was questioned by the two arresting officers, DI Gordon and DC Mellis, then taken down to the cells and put into one which was already occupied by a black man called Ruby, who was out of his head on smack. He was still there when I went in, still out of his head and totally oblivious to the body lying only a few feet away from him. I shook him, wanting to speak to him, but it was a waste of time. His head just lolled. Clearly he was orbiting Planet Happiness and was going to be there for quite some time. Because of the state he was in, however, we could dismiss him as a murder suspect there and then!

At this point Harry and Mo turned up, and so we started the usual procedure which followed an incident like this. Harry asked for all the duty statements, details of everyone who was in the custody area since Pierce was brought in, and the custody records. Mo went to get the scene-of-crimes officer and a photographer, while I formally told everyone that they could not leave the police station until I said it was OK for them so to do. I then decided to interview Stan Fulford, the PC who had found the body. He was an anaemic-looking lad, and he was also incredibly nervous – in fact he looked terrified – so I tried to reassure him that he wasn't a suspect, but a witness. I think that Pierce's must have been the first body he had ever seen, and a suicide is never a pretty sight. I told him we'd take a statement in the station's Interview Room, but Rooney interrupted me, saying that the room was still being used by the two officers who had arrested Pierce. They were currently interviewing Dilly, Pierce's friend, who was making a statement in the presence of his solicitor.

I found another empty room and spoke to PC Fulford in there. He said that he found Pierce hanged at 12.40 am – his previous check had been at 12.05 and Pierce had shown no sign of being depressed or suicidal then. That was all he could tell me. I told him that once the scene-of-crimes officer had taken samples of his hair and clothing, he would be free to go home. I doubted very much whether the kid would get any trouble-free sleep for a long time to come. I knew I wasn't going to. It was going to be a long night, and we were there for the duration. I was eager to speak to the two officers who had arrested Pierce, and as soon as they had finished interviewing Dilly, I asked to see both of them, one at a time.

The first arresting officer to come into my makeshift interview room was DC Mellis, DI Gordon's partner. He looked glum and sullen, and was obviously extremely pissed off that he was not able to go home after a night's hard graft. He told me that Pierce had made no attempt to resist arrest, and had appeared fairly calm during his interview with the two officers back at the station – even though he knew he was being arrested for possessing £500's worth of crack. He had declined the offer of a solicitor and had been detained in the cells for further questioning. That was all Mellis could tell me. I let him go and went in search of some coffee. I found Mo by the machine, and she told me she had just finished speaking with Dilly's solicitor, a rather smart young woman whom Mo had instantly liked. They had had a chat in the canteen – the solicitor had seen Pierce after his interview, on his way to the cells. She thought he seemed shaken and quiet. She also thought he would need a solicitor, so she asked DI Gordon whether she could go down to the cells to speak with him. Gordon had sent Mellis down instead, who reported back that Pierce had again refused the offer of a solicitor. She finished her conversation with Mo by telling her that she hadn't known Pierce, but knew Dilly very well.

We were interrupted by the arrival of PC Hamilton from the Coroner's Office, who had come to take away Pierce's body. I led him to the cells and then went back to the reception desk, where Mr and Mrs Pierce had turned up to collect their son's valuables. The poor people were distraught; Joseph had been their only son. I introduced myself and Mo to them, but all they could do was keep telling us how good their boy had been; how he had never been in any kind of trouble before. I knew we would have to talk to them in a couple of days time, when they were calmer, and I felt desperately sorry for them. They were decent people who had lost their only boy. Sue and I never had the opportunity to think about having children. I wondered then whether things would have turned out any different if we had. I pulled myself back – there wasn't much point in thinking that way. I said that I'd escort Mr and Mrs Pierce back to the police car which would take them home. As we were leaving the station we all saw a coffin being loaded onto the Home Office meat-wagon. It was appalling timing. I saw Mo's face and she looked as sick as I felt. How Mr and Mrs Pierce felt is unimaginable.

When I got back to the station it was time to interview DI Gordon. He was a cocky and unpleasant bastard with cropped hair and a pug face. If I hadn't known he was a detective inspector I would have put him down as a trouble-making yob. I told him I had just seen Pierce's parents and that they had seemed like decent folk. He sneered in reply, told me that if he'd got a quid every time he listened to a mother telling him her son was innocent, he'd be retired by now. I started to dislike the man intensely from that moment on. He told me that he'd caught Pierce with a tin of crack in the side pocket of his jacket, and reckoned he was supplying Dilly. Dilly had been known to Gordon for a long time – from petty crime, nicking bikes as a kid, to dealing with drugs and ABH. Dilly had never been put away and Gordon was just aching for the chance. He reckoned that the tin of crack had given him enough to put Dilly and Pierce away for a long time. He denied roughing up either Pierce or Dilly during their interviews, and thought Pierce had committed suicide because he was frightened of what his drug bosses would do if they knew that he had got caught by the Old Bill with the goods in his possession.

I told Gordon that he could go, but something that Mo had said made me want to interview Mellis again. He appeared even more sullen in this second interview, if that was at all possible. Mo had said that on the solicitor's request, Mellis had gone down to the cells to ask Pierce whether he wanted to see a solicitor. I quizzed Mellis about that. I asked him why the incident wasn't noted in the Incident Report Book. Mellis replied that he had forgotten. I suggested that he had a go at Pierce in the cells. Mellis denied any rough stuff – actually, he was probably telling the truth, since the police doctor didn't find any signs of bruising consistent with a beating.

I was exhausted. It seemed that no one knew anything about Pierce's suicide, or if they did, they certainly weren't going to tell CIB. My eyes felt gritty and grainy, and when I looked out of the window I saw that it was morning. I'd had enough. I told everyone they could go home. When Mo asked me on the way out what my thoughts were about the suicide, I think I made a weak joke and told her I suspected the KGB. Buggered if I knew. I was so tired when I got into my car I didn't think where I was going. I only realised where I was when I had parked it and was going up the stairs into Jenny's flat. When I crawled into bed beside her she didn't push me away. I took this as a good sign, and fell straight asleep.

The next day Mo, Harry and I were all late into the office – but it was a Saturday. I had planned to do my paperwork on the Pierce investigation, but as things turned out, I found my personal life coming under attack from all quarters.

The first I knew of this was when Golden Boy Graves burst into my office, shouting that someone had broken into his office and had gone through his file on the Carswell enquiry. Graves wasn't actually accusing me, but the implication was there. Because I was involved with Jenny, I must be the guilty party. I had had very little sleep the night before, my eyes were still gritty, and I had a headache. I'd had enough of Graves and his spoilt-little-boy manner. I grabbed him around the neck and hauled him into Deakin's office, to get the matter resolved once and for all. Deakin soon dispatched Graves with a few sharp, well-chosen phrases, but when I turned to go he told me to stay. Then I got it all. I was ruining my career by screwing around – more specifically, by screwing WPC Dean, who was under CIB investigation. He suggested that I put a stop to it before I saw my whole career disappear down the toilet.

At first I was incredibly pissed off at finding my personal life was suddenly under such close scrutiny by my bosses. Then I got to thinking a little harder. The reason everybody was leaning so hard on me was because of Jenny's involvement with the Carswell enquiry. It was then that I decided to have a little chat with Harry – he had mates all over the force and could easily do a bit of informal snooping around. And I was eager to find out what was really going on with this Carswell business.

Meanwhile, it was back to the Pierce investigation. The pathologist's report had arrived on my desk and it confirmed that Pierce had died from strangulation. Other than the bruising around his neck and a little around his right wrist, Pierce had a young, healthy, undamaged body. We still didn't know whether he had taken any drugs on the night of his arrest – the blood test results weren't yet available – but no flesh had been found under his nails and there were no signs indicating a struggle apparent on the body. We were coming up with nothing but dead ends. Mo then suggested that we visit Pierce's GP, since she might be able to give us a clue as to the boy's state of mind. Maybe we'd find out that he was a depressive, and that his suicide had been only a matter of time. But we left the GP's surgery feeling more confused than before. She was shocked by the circumstances of Pierce's death – she told us that he was an exceptionally bright boy who had been hoping to study medicine at Manchester University. He had set his heart on becoming a doctor and he had been working hard to achieve that goal. None of the feedback we had on Pierce sounded like he was a disturbed young man on the verge of suicide, so it was back to St Helen's for us, to listen to the tapes of Gordon's interview with Pierce.

They didn't make easy listening. DI Gordon was verbally aggressive and abusive, but we didn't prosecute coppers for having aggressive interview techniques. If we had, though, Gordon would have been the first out of the door. Gordon kept on going back to the tin found in Pierce's pocket. Pierce's argument in return was weak – he didn't know how it got there, but admitted that Gordon took it out of his jacket pocket. As murder was looking so unlikely, suicide was really our only option, but I still wanted to know why. Was Pierce so mentally and physically intimidated by DI Gordon that he committed suicide rather than face police questioning again? Or was he tripping on something, so obsessed by the thought of how badly he had screwed up that suicide was the only route left open to him? I didn't know. I drove back to the office, thinking about it all the way.

It was when I was sitting at my desk, still wondering, that Harry walked in with the info he had gleaned about Jenny and the Carswell enquiry. He told me that she alone probably knew enough to put the other officers away, and that Hargreaves was constantly seen hanging round her, badgering her about something. Harry had also found out from Jenny's sergeant that since being served with the 163, she had become highly strung, upset and emotional. I decided it was time to do something about it all – I was sick and tired of other people manipulating my life. Added to this, I felt sorry and guilty about Jenny. I put in a request to Deakin, asking for formal permission to 'cohabit' with her. Deakin refused. I walked out of his office and the CIB building not knowing if I ever wanted to go back. Then I remembered that Mo and I had arranged to go and see Pierce's parents. I also remembered how devastated they had looked when they came to collect their son's belongings. I knew that I didn't want to let these people down – on this case, at least, I'd find out what really happened. After that ... I didn't know.

Mr and Mrs Pierce lived in a nice house in a nice middle-class area. They offered us tea. They kept telling us what a good boy Joseph had been, how he had never been in any kind of trouble. Mrs Pierce kept breaking down in tears. I wanted to talk to Mr Pierce alone so I asked him to show me Joseph's bedroom. Once upstairs I asked him whether he thought his son did drugs. Mr Pierce informed me that his son had never even smoked. But then I remember thinking, what do parents really know about what their kids get up to? Mine certainly hadn't a clue about half the strokes I pulled at that age. What they didn't know couldn't hurt them, I had thought.

A few days later I was summoned to Huxtable's office. The trimmings of our earlier friendship had fallen away – all that was left now was unease and stilted conversation. He wanted to see me about Jenny Dean. He told me that I could live with her if she gave evidence against Hargreaves and the other officers involved in the Carswell enquiry. That sounded like blackmail to me. I drove straight over to Jenny's flat.

She had prepared a romantic meal for two. The tiny kitchen was steamed up from her efforts – God knows why it was so steamy. I remember to this day that she made guacamole to start with. I ruined the evening. It was effortless, really. I asked her about Eddie Hargreaves, was she still having sex with him? Dinner went on the floor, and once again I left. I drove around aimlessly until I found myself back in Clapham, cruising past my old house. I remember now how desperately I wanted to see Sue, to talk to her and to have her make everything all right for me – I was so confused and it seemed my life had become such a mess. I even rang the doorbell of the house we had bought just after our marriage. She answered. She looked lovely, dressed up in a little black dinner dress. But the expression on her face was one of embarrassment, and it was only then that I noticed the man standing in our hall – her hall. I left.

The following day the lab results came through. The blood tests showed that Pierce had had no more than three pints in his bloodstream, while the tin containing the crack had one set of his prints on it, and one set of DI Gordon's. Inside, the tin was full of Dilly's prints. I drove down to St Helen's, to tell DI Gordon about the forensic evidence. Because the tin hadn't been found on Dilly's person, he wouldn't go down for possession – the one thing that Gordon was really hoping to do him for. I then gave him my theory about Pierce's suicide. I suggested that it came about through fear – fear of letting his parents down, of not going to university, of failing in his ambition to become a doctor. His parents had been right – Joseph Pierce had been a good boy, and loyal to his friends even if those 41 same friends had set him up. He had known Dilly since primary school, and had kept in touch with him even when Dilly had dropped out at the age of thirteen. It was Dilly who had slipped Pierce the tin, letting his friend take the rap for possession.

Gordon was scornful of my interpretation. He refused to hear what I was saying and maintained Pierce's guilt, saying that I was soft to believe what Pierce's parents had told me. I suggested that he could learn from his mistakes, and that next time, given a similar situation, he could go easier. His interviewing techniques, I believed, had finally pushed that terrified kid over the edge. That was how my report would read.

It was then that Gordon lost his cool. He was contemptuous of and angry about my methods – and certainly didn't like his own being criticised. He stormed out of the police station, and I haven't see him since. I don't know where he is now, but I know he holds a grudge against me. Bullies like DI Gordon never forget those who they feel need to be taught a lesson.

Suspect Dossier file No.: 9
Subjects: DEAKIN,
THE URQUHARTS, DENNIS RALSTON
& MARK LUMLEY

Harry was working a late shift when the call came through from King's Cross nick about Detective Superintendent Billy Urquhart. The bold Billy had been caught entertaining a hooker in his car and had arrested by officers (known unofficially as the 'Snatch' Squad) observing the toms plying their trade around the back-streets of the station. Knowing that rumours questioning DS Urquhart's basic honesty had been causing raised eyebrows for years, Harry realised that this arrest would cause a stir. He also saw no reason why he should be the only player on our team not enjoying a good night's sleep and immediately called me.

If he was hoping to wake me from a deep sleep, Harry must have been disappointed. I was wide awake and feeling pretty grim. I had spent most of the evening bickering with Jen about Hargreaves and the Carswell case. She just couldn't seem to see that all she had to do was tell the truth. If that meant that Hargreaves and his sidekicks got their arses booted out of the Met, then that was their problem. They shouldn't have been playing silly buggers fitting up Carswell in the first place. Little did I know that Billy Urquhart was about to drag me into the thick of the Carswell flak as well.

Harry and I met up at King's Cross nick, where we talked to Inspector Capstick, a cool-headed woman who played things by the book and had taken great exception to Urquhart's attitude when he was brought in. He'd told her that he'd have the whole matter squared away in the morning, and had tried to intimidate her by warning her that he knew her guvnor and her guvnor's guvnor and she had better watch her step. Capstick's response had been to throw him in the cells. Seemed reasonable to me. As she filled us in on the details of Urquhart's arrest, Commander Huxtable arrived. Billy Urquhart had always been a name I'd heard bandied about as belonging to someone who was a bit of a rogue. If Huxtable felt that the situation demanded his own personal attention, then perhaps Urquhart was a bigger catch than I had thought.

We all trooped off to an interview room and waited for Urquhart to be delivered from the cells. When he was brought in, Huxtable took over. He formally served notice on Urquhart that an enquiry was being launched into his conduct, and that he was suspended from duty pending the outcome of that enquiry. Almost as an afterthought, he added that Urquhart's home was to be searched. Urquhart's reaction was interesting to watch. He became noticeably agitated, his eyes flitting around the room as if he was checking the place for an escape route. He stammered something about that really not being necessary for a poxy kerb-crawling charge, but Huxtable insisted it was. He was determined to throw the book at Billy Urquhart.

Harry, Mo and I escorted Urquhart back to his house to conduct a search. We were looking for anything that would tie him in to other illegal activities, and even as we drew into his driveway, Urquhart was complaining that the search was right out of order. He was whining on about how, when he had first started, a quick leg-over with one of your beat's working girls was considered to be a perk of the job. No one was listening. We were all too busy taking in his house, or mansion, to be precise. The place was of a size and in a location that reeked of serious money. You wouldn't have been surprised to find that a successful stockbroker or a minor rock star lived there. It certainly wasn't the sort of place you could finance on a Superintendent's salary.

Urquhart's moaning was becoming unbearable as we got out of the car, so I pulled him to one side and told him that I thought there was more to this evening than just a casual naughty. Otherwise, Billy could simply have claimed he was working and told the arresting officer to piss off, but maybe Billy had been trying to get away without being mentioned in the officer's incident report book. Old Billy Boy had something to hide.

Sandra Urquhart met us at the front door. She was an attractive, aggressive, sophisticated woman who didn't take kindly to having her home searched, but seemed well clued up on police procedure and let us get on with it. The Urquhart's had spared no expense in furnishing and decorating their home. Billy was quick to point out that they lived as they did mainly from the proceeds of his wife's business. I remember thinking that she should, therefore, be extremely upset that the bastard had been caught with a tart on the front seat of her Jaguar. Instead, she was giving him nothing but support.

I told Mo to go with Sandra to her study, so that Sandra could explain to Mo the exact nature of her business and how it worked. Mo made copious notes and had such a good grasp of Sandra Urquhart's business by the time we left several hours later that she could probably have taken over as MD. As it turned out, the business relied heavily on the involvement of a senior police officer anyway. Urquhart Recruitment and Personnel Consultancy specialised in recruiting staff to handle cash and sensitive information. Sandra's clients relied on her to supply them with employees who were squeaky clean, scrupulously honest and with no convictions or money problems in their background. Mo reckoned that Sandra's biggest client was Ralston Publications and Leisure, which put thousands of pounds through URPC's books every month. Apart from Mo's findings, we didn't take anything out of Urquhart's house that night except expensive carpet fluff on our shoes.

The next day Huxtable and Deakin joined us in my office for a case conference. Huxtable was desperate for us to give him something more than kerb crawling. I told him that Urquhart was living way above his salary, and Mo filled us all in on Urquhart's wife's biggest client. Dennis Ralston, MD and sole owner of Ralston Publications and Leisure, had convictions for pimping and pornography, but had remained untouched by the law for many years. I reckoned that Urquhart was using his position as a police officer with access to privileged information to tip Ralston off if any of his premises were due for a raid, and to dish the dirt for Ralston on his business rivals. Deakin dismissed what we had so far as conjecture and supposition. We had no evidence. He told us that there had been rumours about Urquhart since his days in Vice in the 70s. It went with the territory. I asked why we had never gone after him before and Harry mumbled something about Urquhart being fireproof. Huxtable hit the roof. He told us that no one was fireproof and that he wanted proof that Urquhart was in Ralston's pocket.

Meanwhile, Graves was grilling Jenny over her involvement in the arrest of Michael Carswell, who had been convicted of the murder of a man called Mace. Mace had been thrown out of a night club by Carswell, the bouncer, then beaten to death in an alleyway. Jenny had been driving the car in which DS Eddie Hargreaves had taken Carswell to the nick after his arrest; in the car, Hargreaves claimed, Carswell had confessed to the murder. Carswell, however, had been released on appeal after two tarts had come forward and sworn blind that Mace was alive and kicking when Carswell left him in the street. The 'confession' Hargreaves and his two DCs claimed to have heard was extremely suspect. Jenny had been drafted in from another area to act as back-up on the day of the arrest, and was only driving Hargreaves because his own car had broken down. That mechanical failure had put poor Jen in an extremely awkward position. Had she heard the confession? To her credit, she told Graves the truth. She hadn't heard Carswell admit to a thing. It was looking bad for Hargreaves and his mates. They had stitched Carswell up and they were going to take the fall for it. Grassing on a fellow officer, of course, made Jenny feel like a real snake. She'd be known forever as the bitch who sold Hargreaves down the river...especially since she'd been sleeping with him. Jealousy being what it is, I had been encouraging Jen to shop Hargreaves, but I was too blind to see the strain she was under. People were pressurising her from all sides, and I was too insensitive to appreciate the effect it was having on her. That's a burden I will carry with me for the rest of my life.

Our next move in the Urquhart fiasco involved Porn King Dennis Ralston. Harry had been digging in the files and had come up with a mountain of paper detailing his sordid little career from his days as a message boy for Soho gangsters, through his period as a pimp and a hustler, to his literary endeavours in the world of glossy magazines and his expansion into the 'movie' business. You don't build an empire like Ralston's without getting your hands dirty, but nobody had been able to pin anything on him for years, even though he was now rumoured to be dealing in drugs as well as depravity.

Harry also turned up a report on the tom Urquhart had picked up in his wife's Jag. Amongst a long list of convictions for prostitution, Linda Jordan was also noted as a witness in the Carswell case. This whole pile of crap was starting to take on a very strange shape. All we could do was keep digging away at the bottom and wait to see who it all fell on. My next bit of spadework had to be with Linda Jordan.

I arrived at King's Cross by taxi, a black cab that the Met used for undercover and surveillance jobs. It wasn't hard to find Linda Jordan. She was waiting at the street corner I'd been told she normally frequented, dressed aggressively in black leather jacket and mini skirt, fishnet stockings and spiked heels, yet somehow managing to look only frail and vulnerable. A red Rover drew up beside her and, after a brief negotiation through the car window, she got in and the car drove off. We followed. When the car pulled up under a quiet railway arch, I gave them long enough to make the situation as awkward as possible, then banged on the roof of the Rover, flashed my warrant card, and told the punter to piss off. Linda Jordan and I had a chat in the taxi.

She made a pretty poor job of denying that she knew Billy Urquhart, claiming that he was just another punter. She was equally unforthcoming about the Carswell enquiry, saying that she and her mate Sheri only came forward because they didn't want to see an innocent man go to jail. I knew she wasn't telling me the whole story. Giving her my card, I dropped her back on her beat.

Ralston was our next port of call. Harry and I drove out to his house deep in the heart of Surrey. If Urquhart's house was a mansion, this place was a palace, albeit a somewhat eccentric one. From the outside it was impressive, an imposing, white-pillared country residence that looked as though it had been plucked straight from the set of 'Gone With the Wind'. By the side of the house was a garage big enough to house several buses, and in front of that was a burly minder, polishing an already immaculate Rolls Royce. As we trundled up the driveway, Ralston, on horseback, appeared from somewhere in the grounds, accompanied by the most beautiful girl I had ever seen. Her gleaming white jodhpurs looked as though they had been sprayed on, and I immediately started to imagine what she would look like naked. As it happened, my curiosity was soon satisfied. When Ralston showed us inside, he sat Harry and me down on a sofa which would have been more at home in a seventeenth-century brothel. On the wall straight in front of us was a massive oil painting of the very same sofa...with Ralston's riding companion draped naked across it.

The interview was amiable and uninformative. We were served tea by a Filipino house boy as Ralston admitted to being a client of Sandra Urquhart but denied being involved in anything improper or illegal. He was a smarmy, self-assured, arrogant bastard and I looked forward to the day when I would flush his dignity down the toilet along with the rest of his sleazy little life. On the way out, the minder at the Roller tripped a switch in Harry's memory. He was a thug called Mark Lumley.

Harry reckoned that the best way to dish the dirt on an officer of Urquhart's rank was to talk to his bagman. We pulled in DS Mercer and both of us interviewed him. Mercer wasn't giving anything away while I was around, so I manufactured an urgent call and left him to Harry. As one bagman to another, Harry was able to lay it on the line to Mercer. We knew that Urquhart had been using Mercer to run checks on the Police National Computer. One check Mercer had made was on a North London newsagent with a conviction for gross indecency. Shortly afterwards, the newsagent was stocking nothing on his 'adult' shelf but Ralston's rags. Harry put it to Mercer that he was being used to obtain information which Urquhart passed to Ralston, who then used it for the purpose of blackmail. Mercer admitted that he had made a few dodgy PNC checks, but claimed that Urquhart would have made life impossible for him if he hadn't done the odd 'no-questions-asked' favour. One thing he had refused to do, though, was to run a check on a man who had no convictions on their patch, a man Urquhart had seemed unduly interested in, a man who was arrested the very next day – Michael Carswell. Now we had Urquhart well and truly tied in to the Carswell case.

No sooner had I left the room than my bogus urgent call turned out to be a real one. Linda Jordan was hysterical, screaming from a call box that she had to see me straight away, and alone. She sounded absolutely terrified, too terrified even to talk on the phone. We arranged the meet and I left. She was still distraught when I pulled up outside the call box from which she had phoned me. Linda told me that she'd got home that morning to find her flatmate, Sheri Donaldson, chopped to pieces in her bed, and that she knew who the murderer was – Mark Lumley. She knew she'd have copped it, too, if she'd been there, and that this was all linked to Carswell and the Mace killing. She and Sheri had been outside the nightclub when Carswell had slung out Mace. Lumley was there with the Roller, taking them to a 'party' at Ralston's place. The girls recognised Mace; he was the man who had introduced them to the delights of the business of prostitution – their pimp, in other words. He recognised them, too, and became abusive. Lumley stepped in and gave his a smack, whereupon Mace starting laying into the Roller with his boots. Incensed, Lumley beat Mace to a pulp and left him dying in the alleyway. The girls legged it out of London until the whole thing blew over but returned to give evidence at Carswell's appeal. They were lying low, waiting until they had enough cash to clear off abroad for a while, but Ralston found them through Urquhart. And Urquhart hadn't been picking her up that night in the Jag, he had been telling her to get out of town before Lumley paid them a visit.

I called in the reported murder and by the time Linda and I had made our way back to her flat, the local CID and uniforms had everything under control. Linda assured me that she would repeat everything she had told me in court and I set the wheels in motion to bring in Lumley and Ralston. There was little doubt that they were going down for a very long time. Mo, Harry and I set off to collar Billy Urquhart once again. Now he wasn't just facing some pathetic kerb crawling charge, now he was looking at a long stretch behind bars for perverting the course of justice, offences under the Data Protection Act, accessory to murder, or maybe even conspiracy to murder. I was going to enjoy shoving all that down his throat.

While Ralston and Lumley were being nicked, we turned up on Urquhart's doorstep in time to catch Billy and Sandra on their way out. Billy, as they say, 'accompanied us to the station', while Sandra stayed at home. She was keen to have a chat with Mo and I was only too happy to leave them together. If anybody could get something out of Sandra to help us put Billy away, it was Mo. In the end, though, her little chat turned out to be much more useful even than that.

Huxtable was over the moon about Urquhart being hauled in again, and left for a weekend in the country with his old mate Dunning, formerly our DAC at CIB but now a Deputy Chief Constable out in the sticks. He left Urquhart to us, and we put him through a mental and verbal grilling. Billy clammed up, refusing to make any further comment. He knew he was deep in the shit, but something about his expression, his eyes, maybe his body language, told me that he still had another major card to play.

I had dinner with Jenny in a restaurant that night. She told me that Hargreaves was leaning on her to change her story to say she got out of the car for a moment, anything that would let his 'confession' fairytale stand up. I warned her not to be taken in by Hargreaves and his mates. The Carswell enquiry looked like it was going to cause a real stink and I told her to stick to her guns or she'd end up in as much shit as the rest of them. Jenny threw a complete fit and stormed out of the restaurant. She wasn't at her flat when I got there. I fell asleep waiting for her and when I woke up the next morning she still hadn't come home. I thought that this time I had really screwed things up. I had been right out of order the night before, carping on and on about Hargreaves and the Carswell thing. I was angry at Jen for taking it all so desperately seriously, and angry at myself for not being more understanding towards her. I was also pissed off at the thought of all the effort that would have to go into making up again.

The next day, at lunchtime, having spent a frustrating morning pushing paper around and phoning half of London to try to find Jenny, I was on my way to the pub to meet Harry when Mo intercepted me and dragged me into a café for a word. Sandra Urquhart had been most informative during their girlie chat. Her dear old hubby wasn't the only senior policeman taking backhanders from Ralston. There was someone higher up, watching Ralston's back, keeping things sweet. Mo handed me a photo Sandra had given her as a teaser. It was of a group of black ties at a boxing dinner. Ralston was there, so was Urquhart, and standing right beside them was Deputy Chief Constable Trevor Dunning.

I reported straight back to Deakin. His first reaction was to tell me not to be so stupid. There was no way we could go after our boss's best mate, the man tipped to become the next Metropolitan Commissioner. I explained that those were my thoughts exactly, until I considered how bad it would look if anyone involved in the Carswell mess – Ralston, Urquhart, Lumley, or even an investigating officer, offered up Dunning as Mr Big. CIB would look like whitewash artists and we could all be out of a job. Deakin allowed himself to be persuaded that Dunning should be investigated, providing that Sandra Urquhart came up with something more substantial than one iffy snapshot. Then he told me I was off the case. My relationship with Jenny had meant that I couldn't be involved in the Carswell investigation and now that all this appeared to be tied in, I'd have to pass the parcel on this one, too.

I was furious. It seemed like nothing could go right for me. My whole life was a mess. Things just couldn't get any worse, and then they did. I knew by the look on Harry's face when he walked into my office that he was bringing me bad news. He did his best to break it gently, but it still hit me like a blow from a hammer. Jenny was dead. She'd committed suicide.

The next few days are all a bit of a blur to me. I couldn't eat and I couldn't sleep, but I couldn't really say I was awake, either. I wandered around in a complete daze. Sometimes I found myself walking down the street, crying, suddenly realising where I was, but not quite knowing how I got there. No amount of drink seemed to have any effect. I had been responsible for ruining Jenny's life, driving her to despair, never giving her the comfort she needed. When I'd last seen her we'd had a furious row. Was that what she was thinking about when she drank herself insensible and threw herself off the back of a riverboat? I'll never know. Worst of all, I never had the chance to say goodbye.

At Jenny's funeral, I sneaked in late, not wanting to cause too much fuss. By the time it was all over, I felt I should do the right thing and speak to Jenny's sister and her father. We all grieved for her, after all. They didn't want to know me. Her father, especially, held me in utter contempt. They could hardly be expected to realise how much I was hurting, I suppose.

There were another couple of familiar faces at the crematorium. One was DS Eddie Hargreaves, lurking up at the back. We didn't speak. We didn't have to: one lingering look of complete loathing said it all. The other was Deakin. He met me outside and offered to take me out to get drunk – I believe it was a genuine offer, too. I declined. I wanted to get back to work and put all this behind me. He told me to take some leave. I wasn't wanted back at CIB. Neither was Huxtable for that matter. He was too close to Dunning to be seen to be impartial, so he was off on leave as well. I had no choice but to take an enforced holiday. There was no way, however, that I was going to lose touch with what was going on.

Regular meetings with Mo and Harry kept me up to date. Sandra Urquhart had handed over the contents of a bank safety-deposit box to Mo: Bank account details, payments, expenses, a whole raft of stuff, some of which was deniable, some of which would leave Dunning sorely wounded. DCC Dunning, meanwhile, was outraged. He'd been suspended and, on the basis that he'd lost his credibility, he was convinced that his career was over. He didn't have to worry about becoming Metropolitan Commissioner any more, just staying out of jail would be a result. Chief Constable Gordon of Wessex Constabulary was supervising the investigation, with Deakin handling the nuts and bolts. To begin with, they didn't get much from Dunning during his interviews at CIB. A building society account the Urquharts said was set up by them for him, which he accessed using an autoteller card could, as Dunning pointed out, have been set up for anyone smart enough to remember the PIN. It seemed obvious to Dunning that the Urquharts were trying to buy themselves a deal by setting him up with a whole shitload of spurious evidence.

There was nothing spurious about Dawn Wilding, though. Deakin had photos of Dunning with Wilding, wining and dining her in a posh hotel. Dunning claimed that they had just happened to be staying in the same place, both attending different conferences in a strange town. When pressed, he admitted to indulging in a casual legover with Wilding. He was then told that Wilding was a high class tart, sent by Ralston to keep Dunning's feet warm. The tab for the champagne they were drinking in the hotel bar, and in her bedroom, was also being picked up by Ralston. Dunning claimed she had told him that she could swing all that on her company expenses. She didn't tell him her company was Ralston Publications and Leisure. Now Dunning's marriage was on the line, as well as his job and his liberty.

I had decided to spend my leave on an activity holiday – with my activities revolving around Eddie Hargreaves. His story for CIB now included an incident where Jenny had got out of the car to scrape some birdshit off the windscreen. During those brief moments, Carswell was supposed to have confessed, or at least said enough for Eddie to embroider it into a confession when he was pressured into doing so by Urquhart and Dunning. Jen was no longer around to deny leaving the vehicle and Hargreaves was neatly deflecting the blame upwards. He would still lose his job, but he'd probably stay out of jail. I reckoned that Jenny had spent her last night with Lucky Eddie and that he, not me, had pressurised her to the extent that she had come to feel that life no longer seemed worth living.

I started keeping an eye on Eddie, tailing him and staking out his Docklands warehouse flat. When he left there on foot one afternoon, I followed him, losing sight of him in a deserted warehouse only to have him try to kebab me on the prongs of a forklift truck. He was pretty handy with that thing, cornering me in a loading-bay and dismounting with the intention of finishing me off. We were in the process of kicking the shit out of each other when a squad car cruised by and we decided to leg it. During the fight several things had become clear. Hargreaves wasn't quite the low-life I expected. I suspect he may even have cared for Jenny. I believed him when he said he hadn't been the last one to talk to Jenny about Carswell – Deakin had. He'd harassed her mercilessly, and had had a meeting arranged with her immediately prior to her taking that ride on the riverboat. Deakin wanted Jen to change her story. As we nursed our wounds in a nearby pub, Hargreaves told me that Deakin was badgering Jenny to tell CIB that she had stepped out of the car, heard Carswell mumble something – anything to back up Hargreaves's load of old bull. Hargreaves wouldn't tell me how he knew all this, and he wasn't telling me everything. Jen was gone, his job was gone, this wasn't his problem any more. He was a tough guy, and he was frightened. Never mind the warehouse brawl, with Deakin on the other side I knew I had a real fight on my hands – and Deakin had proved that he could fight dirty.

I arranged to meet Mo. I needed her to help me find out what the hell was going on and, if we were going up against Deakin, to help me persuade Harry to come on board. Harry had worked for Deakin before and liked him as a boss. Deakin had a reputation for being harsh but fair, and Harry liked that. Mo was with me in wanting to get to the bottom of the affair, so we called Harry to a ridiculously cloak-and-dagger meeting beside the river. I laid it all out for Harry. We suspected that the one watching Urquhart's back was Deakin, not Dunning; that Deakin had laid elaborate plans, stretching back years and including the Dawn Wilding affair, to stitch up Dunning as the man at the top; that by getting rid of Dunning and, in the process, tarnishing Huxtable, Deakin would gain accelerated promotion, perhaps even as far as Commissioner; and that by turning our backs on this, we would be letting a decent man rot in jail while that devious bastard, Deakin, was rolling in clover. Harry was torn. His sense of loyalty to Deakin, who had been good to him over the years, wouldn't let him believe that it could all be true. Finally, however, once he'd bounced it around enough, he could see that someone had been manipulating the whole Carswell pantomime right from the start – and that someone just had to be Deakin. Harry was in, but he warned us that we would only ever get one shot at Deakin, so we had better get it right first time.

The only two men whom I knew I could trust at CIB now were the two poor sods with their heads on the chopping block, though one was admittedly slightly nearer the axe. I approached Huxtable first as a route to Dunning. Huxtable knew where to find his old friend and, having been able neither to offer him assistance up to now nor even go near him, he was only too glad to take me to him. We found Dunning strolling in the woods near his home, carrying a loaded shotgun. Not the right sort of accessory for a man in his state of mind. His morose mood lifted, however, when we explained why we had come. Dunning had suspected Deakin of being on the take for years, but needed the power he would have had when he returned to London as Commissioner to sort out the little rat. Deakin had so many Met officers under his influence that Dunning had never been sure whom he could trust. He couldn't offer us much in the way of proof, and if we tried to go public with our suspicions, Deakin would simply claim that Dunning was uttering the last desperate gasp of a drowning man. We had to move secretly and fast. I already had an idea about that.

Early the next day, Harry met with Deakin on a wet and windy Waterloo Bridge. He explained that he'd asked for the meet in order to pass on some 'sensitive' information to Deakin, information too hot to be whispered in a corridor somewhere at CIB. I was now gunning for Deakin, Harry said, and spilled the whole story: how I suspected Deakin of being involved with Urquhart and Ralston and knew he had intimidated Jenny Dean. He also told him I had a tape of Deakin conversation with Jenny hidden away at home. Deakin thanked Harry, doubtless thinking, that's what old friends are for.

It didn't take Deakin long to act. I left home the next morning and drove round the corner, where I sat and waited while Harry and Mo kept watch on my front door from a van parked across the road. After a couple of hours it was beginning to look as though our plan had fallen through, but then Harry spotted someone he recognised lurking in the street – Ralston's Filipino house-boy. Having checked that the coast was clear, Ralston's man approached my door, picked the lock and was inside in seconds. Deakin had taken the bait Harry had dangled under his nose. The Filipino had to be searching for the tape on Deakin's orders. I just prayed he would find it. I thought I'd done a pretty good job of taping it below a loose floorboard. I needn't have worried. He was out of there in less than five minutes, not long enough for him not to have found what he was looking for. Having captured his arrival and departure on film, Mo followed him as far as Westminster Underground station. Harry accompanied me in the car, then as soon as our target went into the station, they swapped roles, with Harry tailing him on the tube while we raced across town from station to station to pick up the trail when he emerged.

He surfaced at Tower Hill. Mo and I dumped the car and, posing as tourists complete with a video camera, we followed our target past the Tower of London and down to the waterside, where he hopped on a boat taking sightseers across to the floating World War II museum piece, HMS Belfast. Having followed at a discreet distance, we managed to miss the boat. We had a couple of minutes to wait for the next one so Mo filmed the target boarding the Belfast while Harry, who had seen what was going down, started pounding across Tower Bridge to try to get there quicker. The Belfast had to be where Ralston's man was handing the tape over to Deakin. He couldn't possibly be stashing it there for Deakin to collect later. There was no way Deakin would risk leaving what, if it was found, would look like a "suspect" package aboard a military vessel called the Belfast. Deakin had to be on board.

By the time we reached the ship, the little Oriental had vanished. The Belfast is such a maze of decks and gangways that he could have been anywhere. Mo headed upstairs to find a vantage point, while I alerted one of the ship's officers as to what was happening. He assured me that no one would leave the ship without my say-so. My personal radio then crackled and Mo's voice called out that she could see the Filipino on deck with Deakin. The handover was going down and she had it all on film. I raced out on deck and spotted Deakin, but he seemed to be miles away on the vast foredeck of the Belfast. He had also spotted Mo, realised that something was up and was heading for the side, intent on dumping the tape in the Thames. I dashed towards him as he blundered, almost comically, into a crowd of schoolkids, who held him up long enough for me to get there, along with a thoroughly knackered Harry, and grab hold of him. He put up a hell of a struggle, but Harry finally managed to pin his arms to his sides and I snatched the tape.

I arrested him for conspiracy to commit burglary, dishonestly handling stolen goods, conspiracy to pervert the course of justice, and resisting arrest – it was all I could think of at the time. He glared at me and warned me that I'd better get it 100 per cent right between there and the Old Bailey, or he'd find enough loopholes for me to knit a hammock. So I belted him and let him know that the tape was completely blank. He'd panicked and dropped himself right in it, all for sixty minutes of static, but maybe it meant that poor old Jen hadn't died for nothing. Without even being there, she'd brought about Deakin's arrest.

Having blown the Carswell case wide open, I guess that there are a good few names to add to my list of potential assassins. Billy Urquhart must be feeling a little peeved that I managed to slash through his carefully prepared safety net. His wife, having lost her husband and struggling to keep her hands on her other treasured possessions, probably doesn't have my name at the top of her Christmas card list, either. Dennis Ralston and Mark Lumley might normally prefer a more direct approach than a few chicken-shit melodramatic letters shoved through my letterbox. But then again, maybe they're just keeping me guessing until they have the opportunity to walk the streets again and come to visit me one day for that personal touch. I suppose the Filipino and his wife, both of whom worked for Ralston, must be feeling bitter that I've destroyed the nice little number they had set up for themselves at Ralston Towers. I wouldn't exclude them completely.

But the one who took a big hit on this caper and who I know really wants me dead is Deakin. Silly letters might not seem to be his style, but the man is so devious that this can't be discounted as one of his crazy schemes. He's already tried to arrange for my untimely departure once, and I've no doubt that he will try again. I won't stop looking out for Deakin until I see the bastard lying on a mortuary slab.

Suspect Dossier file No.: 10
Subject: JOE RANCE

Life was very different for me after the arrest of Deakin on the HMS Belfast. I should say life was very different without Jenny, but it wasn't really. I hate to admit it, but her death brought a kind of release, while the whole incident with Deakin on the ship served to close that chapter of my life. Of course, he was still awaiting trial, and there was the possibility that he would walk, but I doubted it. Our case against him had been fireproof. And in the meantime I was made acting Chief Super. I had put the existing one away, after all.

Mo was trying really hard to cheer me up at that time. She even let me into Harry's big secret – he was heavily into ballroom dancing. I wouldn't have believed it if I hadn't seen it with my own eyes – the forty-fags-a-day man waltzing with his missus around Streatham Ballroom. And they even won their heat. Life was full of surprises. I had even given up smoking.

Back at CIB, everything went on much the same as ever – there were still bent coppers out there, which meant we were never out of work. A new file had arrived on my desk which needed urgent and delicate investigation, as the matter was racially sensitive. I briefed Harry and Graves. My feelings towards Graves hadn't changed – I still thought him a smug bastard – but for the time being I was his boss. I was, therefore, determined to make him squirm for as long as I could. I really did my damnedest to rub his nose in it. Looking back, I now realise that pride really does come before a fall. I was about to take a major tumble.

The case we were investigating centred around Bold Road Police Station. A squad had been called out one night to deal with a riot that had broken out outside a mosque in their area. A group of skinheads had stuck a pig's head on top of the minaret, but were spotted by the local Asians, who attacked their van. The skinheads retaliated by chucking Molotov cocktails, and by the time the police arrived some serious fighting had broken out. We had been called in because in all this fighting an Asian – Mr Khan, the caretaker of the mosque – had witnessed a policeman collaring a skinhead. The skinhead said something to the officer, who then let him go. Mr Khan had seen all this quite clearly, so much so that he had even got the policeman's number – PC537. It didn't take much detective work for us to find out that the number was that of PC Tulloch of Bold Road nick. And so that's where I told Harry and Graves to go.

PC Tulloch stood accused of neglect of duty and failing to make an arrest. Harry and Graves reported later that they didn't get much out of him. Tulloch's argument was that he had attempted to arrest the skinhead but that the yob had broken loose and he had then noticed that Mr Khan appeared to be in some trouble, so went over to him to make sure he was all right. This had sounded like a pretty unconvincing story to Harry and Graves, and on further questioning it turned out that PC Tulloch wasn't exactly sympathetic to the Asian cause anyway – he complained to Harry and Graves that the Bold Road coppers were always being called out to the mosque for what he considered to be the most trivial of reasons. He didn't seem to think that the Asian population had the same right as other citizens to go about their business peaceably, or to enjoy the protection of the police.

I decided to see Tulloch myself. Whether it was because of my senior rank, or perhaps that I looked more aggressive than Harry or Graves, Tulloch at least gave me something more to go on. The reason he had let the skinhead go was because he had recognised him. The two of them had been cadets together at Hendon. Tulloch gave us the skinhead's name – Joe Rance. Rance was a serving police officer. Now I knew we had opened up a real can of worms.

Later on that evening Harry and I went out for a game of pool. It seemed to me that the whole Jenny Dean/Deakin affair had brought us closer together. We'd occasionally go for a boy's night out – something we had never done before. Sadly, all that had to change when we found out about Harry's wife and how ill she was, but that was later. That night we were drinking pints – I may have given up smoking but I hadn't given up drinking after all – and talking about Graves. Harry told me that Graves had boasted to him about being selected for a possible promotion. I remember telling Harry I'd be delighted if Graves got it – it would mean he'd be out of our offices and out of our lives for good. My own promotion hadn't been confirmed yet; at the time I supposed that my seniors were waiting for the outcome of Deakin's trial. As we talked, I glanced up at the TV on the wall. On screen was a very right-wing politician – the backbencher Douglas Carter – defending the Home Office's decision to allow the controversial historian Patrick Ingram into the country. Ingram was the author of a book called A Twentieth Century Myth, in which he denied that the Holocaust had ever happened. A lot of people, myself included, found him offensive in the extreme. Over in the States, where he was based, he had incited mobs to attack Jews, beat up blacks and burn down mosques. It reminded me of the Bold Street affair. Racial hatred and fascist sympathies seemed to be growing on both sides of the Atlantic. It was frightening.

The next day Mo and I paid a visit to the Law Courts. It was the first day of Deakin's trial. We all knew that he wasn't going to go down without a fight, but we were both stunned at the lengths to which he went to discredit us. He said that on the day of his arrest he had received a phone call from an informant who claimed to have in his possession incriminating evidence about a senior police officer. Deakin agreed to meet the man – but didn't tell any of his colleagues where he was going because of the atmosphere of distrust that permeated the CIB offices. Black mark against us. He then went on to say that he had resisted arrest on board HMS Belfast because he had panicked, for it was then, he said, that he realised he had been set up. In effect, the only charge to which he was going to plead guilty was that of assault whilst resisting arrest. Mo and I left the court absolutely gobsmacked.

Back at CIB another surprise awaited me. Graves told me he wanted me to take over the Joe Rance investigation – the whole affair was beginning to look sensitive and he wanted someone senior to handle it. I suspected that the only reason he passed the case back to me was because he was too busy with his promotional board to put much work into the investigation himself. It didn't bother me. I got Mo to take over and she threw herself into investigating Rance with impressive vigour. She also established how politically hot the investigation was turning out to be.

She had started by going to Rance's home station, where she talked to his commanding officer. All he would say was that Rance was on extended sick leave – his chief hadn't seen him for months. She then went to his home address. There was no answer when she rang the bell but a neighbour came out to tell her that Rance hadn't been seen in months – however, a woman still came in most mornings to pick up his mail and dust the flat. The following day Mo intercepted the cleaner as she came up the garden path. She seemed extremely reluctant to talk to Mo, telling her cagily that Rance was travelling and she just kept an eye on his flat and his mail. She told Mo that her name was Judy Prescott – and then produced her warrant card. Judy Prescott was a sergeant in Special Branch. That's when Mo suggested that she come over to New Scotland Yard with her boss to talk to us.

The meeting turned out to be highly informative. We got all the information we needed about Joe Rance. Special Branch told us that Rance was an educated and intelligent young policeman who had infiltrated a fascist organisation. He had a first-class degree in politics and was totally dedicated to his job. Previously he had gone undercover for CID, posing as a football hooligan. He had really taken on the part: shaved head, big boots, Union Jack T-shirt. Many of the hooligans he had come into contact with were 'Friends of the Movement' and so Rance had joined that fascist party too, rapidly progressing through the ranks. The national organiser, a man called Derek Lee Metford, had taken a shine to Rance and had admitted him into the secret membership of an elite group called 'New Order'. Rance's reports indicated that the organisation was grooming him for great things.

I was finding it very hard to swallow all this, because I believed Rance was now in way over his head and, judging by his violent behaviour at the mosque, had probably gone native. Mo agreed with me – he was a young, impressionable copper after all. Third-hand intelligence, however, would never give us anything to back up our argument. I wanted to interview Rance so I could judge for myself on which side of the fence he'd planted his Doc Martens. Judy Prescott's boss, Inspector Cole, refused permission point blank. He argued that to pull Rance out at this sensitive stage in the operation – they had had notification that something big was going down, involving the visit of Patrick Ingram – would jeopardise months of hard work. I was unmoved. Rance was subject to the law, just like any other UK citizen, and he had been accused of violent assault. I lost my rag in the meeting and told Sergeant Prescott and Inspector Cole that if they didn't allow me access to Rance, I'd be sure to charge them for obstructing the course of justice. I think that Cole was by then on the verge of punching me out, when Mo came up with a compromise. She asked the two Special Branch officers whether we could talk to Rance in the field. It seemed like a good solution, and they agreed to arrange something for that same night.

Meanwhile I asked Harry to make some discreet enquiries amongst his Special Branch friends, as I wanted to know what was really going on with Rance and his involvement with New Order. I had a feeling that Special Branch hadn't been entirely straight with us. The great thing about Harry was that he seemed to know everyone in and connected with the force, and that included informants and journalists. Within a couple of hours he had got back to me with more information on what New Order was really about.

Harry had gone down to the East End to talk to his old mate, Norman, who was the editor of a left-wing magazine, *Torchlight*. The magazine did things like name prominent ex-Nazis residing in the UK, and also printed stories of how our fascist police force beat up blacks and Asians. But like everybody else, Norman thought Harry was OK. Norman knew all about New Order – he told Harry that MI5 were also interested in the group because of its Ulster Loyalist connections. And he had done some research on Joe Rance. The twenty-four-year-old was responsible for a string of offences in the East End of London – fire-bombing a synagogue in Stamford Hill, burgling and vandalising a Bangladeshi advice centre in Tower Hamlets, and punching a Trotskyite news-seller in Whitechapel Market were the most recent ones. Norman explained to Harry that to gain entry into New Order, you had to prove yourself. You had to show that you had bottle. You had to show that you were a man of violence. When Harry told me this, we both agreed that Joe Rance had gone native. His activities were straying well outside his brief. There is no way that a police officer, even in deep cover, can ever be sanctioned to commit criminal offences, let alone behave like a nutter, as Rance was.

Harry then gave me his final piece of information. Norman had talked to him about Patrick Ingram, saying that New Order were very sympathetic to his beliefs. Even though the Home Office had warned the historian against indulging in provocative behaviour when he entered England, Ingram was planning to make a speech at a fascist rally in a couple of days time. As yet Norman didn't know where the rally was due to be held, but promised to tell Harry just as soon as he found out. I told Harry to let me know. I wanted to be there when Ingram stood up to say his piece.

The next day, Harry and I went to court. We arrived in time to hear Deakin declared 'not guilty'. Deakin then made a statement, thanking friends and family for their support, and adding that, on medical advice, he felt that he had to resign from the police force. We were stunned. Our weeks of hard work – Jenny's death – had been for nothing. Deakin had shown us that even when at rock-bottom, he was still fireproof. He walked free from the court, and I felt sick to my stomach.

I couldn't afford to dwell on the outcome and the implications for too long, as that evening Graves and I had arranged to meet Joe Rance. Waterloo Bullring seemed an appropriate setting. The place stank, keeping most people away, and it was cloaked in darkness, apart from a few rubbish fires lit by dossers to keep warm. Trains would scream overhead occasionally. It was grim; a fitting meeting place. Rance materialised out of one of the darkened arches. He looked just how I had imagined – hard, brutal. He told us straight off that he thought the meeting was putting his cover at risk, and that he would put that in his final report. He had nothing to say about the mosque incident, and he finished by declaring that he'd talk to us only when the operation was finished. I wasn't convinced. I told him he could pull out there and then if he felt that he was becoming submerged in the culture of New Order. Rance replied he had nothing to get off his chest – he still knew right from wrong. Remembering the list of offences attributed to him, I wasn't so sure. I believed him to be out of control and really wanted to bring him in – irrespective of the fact that it might jeopardise the Special Branch operation. Unsurprisingly, Graves was on the side of Special Branch, saying our investigation could wait. I wondered then whether his promotion was going to be to Special Branch, but let him know that for the foreseeable future I was his boss and he'd have to listen to me. Both of us then went home to our empty beds. At least, I assumed Graves's was empty. He was such a cold fish that I couldn't imagine him with anyone.

The following evening Harry received a call from Norman, who had found out that the venue for Ingram's meeting was going to be the Walker Library in the East End. He'd heard that Ingram might be smuggled into the library disguised as a policeman. The rally had been organised by New Order and essentially had the blessing of the local police, the latter being obliged to make sure that this private meeting took place without the whole thing turning into World War Three. They had gone along with the idea of smuggling Ingram into the meeting dressed as a copper. How else could he and his entourage have got genuine uniforms and a squad car?

Mo, Harry and I shot down to the East End. We didn't want to miss a thing. Outside the library a disturbance had already begun. Behind the police barricades protesters with placards were jeering loudly, screaming for Ingram to go home. I told Mo to join that mob. Harry had persuaded Norman to get him a pass, so he went off with the fascists and skinheads to take his place in the lecture room at the library. Outside it was beginning to get ugly. I could see that the police were having problems in holding the mob back. I saw Norman arguing with one officer on horseback. He was shouting, trying to make himself heard over the noise of the crowd. He was arguing that the hall in the library had been booked under a false name and that the local council would not have given its permission for the library to be used had they known the purpose of the meeting, for the council made it a policy not to give a platform to fascists. The duty officer on the scene shouted back that he was more concerned with the public order offences being committed outside in the street. It was then that Graves and I saw the barricades sway and go down. The mob surged forward, towards the library. It was mayhem. Then I remembered that Mo was in amongst that lot – under my orders. It was impossible for me to get in there and rescue her. I just had to hope that she would be all right.

Graves and I headed towards the rear of the library, figuring that the rear exit was Ingram's only possible escape route. As fighting erupted in the library, we rushed around just in time to see Ingram being hustled into a van, protected by a bunch of skinhead minders. I recognised Rance immediately. It was predictable that he would be there, the most trusted son of New Order looking after Ingram, making sure he came to no harm. We weren't the only ones who had worked out Ingram's emergency plan – there was a handful of protesters braying at him as Rance loaded him into the back of the van. When a photographer got too close, Rance's response was to punch him out. I went for him – but not before he had decked poor old Norman, Harry's contact.

I nicked him. He tried to get away so I made sure I held on even harder. I pinned him against the side of the police van and searched him with Harry's help. It was under his T-shirt that I discovered the mini-tape. Rance had been wired. He was recording the meeting inside. Maybe he had been telling the truth. Maybe he hadn't gone native. I still didn't believe a word he said. What I did know was that I had screwed up Special Branch's operation. What with that and Deakin's walking out of court I knew then that I could kiss my promotion goodbye. I would be lucky if I still had a job the next morning.

Back at CIB, Mo, Harry and I discussed what operation it was we had blown. Harry thought that Special Branch were on to a senior public figure – a politician who had sympathies with Ingram and who was going to talk to him in secret after the Walker library meeting. Somebody like Douglas Carter, MP, perhaps? Possibly. I didn't know. I just knew that I had seriously messed up – Rance had called me a tosser when I had arrested him, and he was only the first in a long line of people who would be spitting fire at me over my performance in this affair.

I later found out that no disciplinary action was going to be taken against Rance, because he resigned from the police force. Although he had committed a series of brutal assaults he wasn't going to be prosecuted, as the Crown Prosecution Service considered that it would not be in the public's interest to do so. Rumour has it that Rance then joined MI5 and that he may have been working for them all along, recruited by them straight from university.

To this day I still believe he had turned native. I remember my meeting with him down at Waterloo. As much as he was trying to convince me he hadn't gone under, everything about him, his gestures, actions and fervour, convinced me otherwise. He was passionate – and extremely dangerous. And he kept company with a lot of dangerous friends. I blew his cover – whether for MI5 or for New Order, I don't know. But I'm sure he must want me dead.

Suspect Dossier file No.: 11
Subject: DAVID LINDSAY

I was right about my promotion. The fiasco over the Joe Rance affair meant I wasn't confirmed as Chief Super. Instead, Graves was. Graves – my new boss. My first reaction was to wish that I hadn't investigated Deakin quite so thoroughly. Anything was better than this university ponce running our outfit. For the time being, however, I was stuck with him, and although I thought it would choke me, I determined to carry on as before, except that now I was calling Graves 'Sir'. It was character-building, to put it mildly. I had said that pride always comes before a fall, hadn't I?

The first investigation under my new boss was the Lindsay case. I remember it well – it took place in March of last year. One of the reasons I remember it the way I do is because Mo was left so devastated by the end of it, and because I realised that we had let a cold-blooded murderer off the hook. We had had insufficient evidence to pin the murder on him. I also remember that during the investigation we left no stone unturned. Harry, Mo and I devoted hours and hours to the case – towards the end because we wanted so badly to nail the bastard, but at the beginning because the alternative to investigating Lindsay was to sift through hundreds upon hundreds of notebooks and duty logs from Argyle Street nick, one of the largest police stations in the UK. Graves, in his new position, was obviously keen to impress his superiors and had undertaken to clear the police force of any corruption or overtime scams that happened to come his way. We were informed that once we had finished the Lindsay investigation we could tackle the Argyle Street job. I was buggered if I was going to waste my time checking up on coppers who had fiddled their expenses and mileage allowances, so I told Harry and Mo we were going to have to spend hours and possibly weeks investigating David Lindsay and the circumstances which led to his wife's death. Not surprisingly, they agreed with me.

David Lindsay had rung his boss in the middle of the night, informing him that he had had a row with his wife and had accidentally killed her – she was lying dead in their living room. I was called in during the early hours of the morning, which seems always to be the way. I got dressed, and think I said goodbye to some blonde who was helping me overcome those long lonely hours in my bed. I don't remember her name – she really wasn't that important.

I drove across London to Detective Super David Lindsay's house. By the time I arrived he had been taken away to Fleet Road nick, where he was being held until he was charged with committing a crime. Manslaughter, probably. However, at his place, it was a circus. It seemed that half of North London had converged at his house – just as I was entering a WPC and a blonde woman were leading two children away. His kids, I guessed.

I was met in the house by Detective Chief Superintendent Powers from the area's Major Investigations Pool. That meant only one thing. We had been double-booked – Graves had called me out of bed quite unnecessarily. I assumed that it was him getting his own back on me, so I determined to ruin his beauty sleep by phoning him on the mobile. Although not best pleased at having been woken at 3.30 am, he asked me to put him on to Powers. When Powers came off the phone he was grinning from ear to ear. Apparently Graves had insisted it was a CIB matter and that I should handle the case. Powers could go home. Before he went, he told me to go easy on David Lindsay. Lindsay was one of his men, and a good bloke who normally would never have hurt his wife. He must have been seriously provoked.

I was left with Mo and Harry, who had joined me at the house, and Detective Constable Minton, an exhibits officer. He was collecting the debris that surrounded the body off the living-room carpet – a smashed plant pot, a coffee-stained cushion, two glasses, and a Radio Times which was covered in blood. Mo, Harry and I retired to the kitchen. It was there that Mo noticed that the washing-machine door was partially open. When she looked inside she found a half empty gin bottle. It must have been put in there only a couple of hours ago – it would never have survived the fast spin cycle. Mo gave it to Minton. I then told my lot to go home, but as Mo lived a few miles past Fleet Road Police Station, I asked her to drop in to inform Lindsay and the Duty Sergeant there that we'd be around the next day at about 11 am to interview Lindsay.

Mo told me next morning that when she had arrived at the station, Lindsay was in the cells, asleep. He had just killed his wife. I would have thought that sleep was the last thing on his mind. I should have realised then that I was dealing with a cold character.

The following day, Mo and I interviewed Lindsay at Fleet Road in the presence of his solicitor. He told us in detail the events of the previous night. He and his wife Dawn, had been due to go to dinner with some of their good friends, the Kings. He had got home after 7pm and found Dawn depressed – the kids were fighting around her and she wasn't doing anything to stop them. Lindsay said that his wife had been depressed for some time – at least for seven months. Several months back he had been investigating a particularly gruesome killing in Kentish Town, in which a young woman had been murdered and disembowelled. It had affected him, turning him right off sex. Since then he'd only had sex with his wife on three occasions. The situation had deteriorated as Dawn grew more distant and depressed. Sometimes she was angry – as when he had got home on the evening in question. Seeing the mood she was in, he'd fed the kids and put them to bed, and then cancelled their dinner date – the third time with that couple. I asked Lindsay whether he was angry with his wife. He told us that he wasn't.

At that point we took a break. I left the interview room, as I had seen Harry arrive and knew he wanted a word with me. Over coffee he told me that he'd been talking to some of the coppers at the nick where Lindsay had been based. Everyone agreed he was a private man – cool and collected, hard-working and ambitious. And as Harry put it, he wasn't a crumpet man. A cold fish, more like.

I went back to the interview room. Mo was already waiting to switch on the tape. Our interview resumed. Lindsay said that after he had put the kids to bed he went back downstairs to talk to Dawn. This was around 8.30. The gin bottle was out. They both had a drink and then they rowed – over his mother, money, his being married to the job. At this stage in the interview I still felt some sympathy for him. I knew how it was and how he felt; I'd been there myself only quite recently. He continued. At 10 pm he went into the kitchen to fix dinner for the two of them. Dawn was totally apathetic and hadn't moved from her chair all evening. He decided to hide the gin bottle in the machine – he didn't want her angry and drunk. They ate dinner and then at around midnight he fell asleep while watching the television. Lindsay told us that this made Dawn really mad – she saw it as proof that he didn't care for her, no longer loved her. He then suggested going to bed, and that's when Dawn flipped. She threw a potted plant across the room, saying that their relationship was a sham. He tried to calm her, hold her, and it was then that she told him she had a lover. She wouldn't stop shouting at him. He strangled her ... Lindsay couldn't go on. I suggested that we break for the day. The poor bloke needed a rest. I looked over to Mo. Her face was like thunder. I decided then to haul her over to the pub and ask her what was eating her.

Once settled with a drink, Mo exploded. She could see he was angling for a conviction for manslaughter rather than being hit with a murder rap. For manslaughter, she said, Lindsay would get two years – the same sentence as for shop-lifting. But if she had it her way he'd be castrated and get fifteen years. I was completely taken aback. I don't think that I'd ever seen Mo get quite as passionate about anything that had come up in our line of work before. She went on to say that women could never use the same argument as men – they just weren't strong enough to strangle a man in the heat of the moment. They could never use their strength as a murder weapon – they'd have to get a knife. And that was the difference between manslaughter and murder. The act of going into the kitchen, finding a knife and returning to carve somebody up with it suggested that some thought had gone into the process, that it was premeditated, that it could only be murder. I gently pointed out that so far we had just interviewed Lindsay, and as yet, we hadn't charged him with anything.

Back at CIB we pulled Lindsay's old file – the one concerning the disembowelment which had disturbed him so much that it had put him off sex. It made horrible reading. More interesting, though, was the write-up by Lindsay of another case he had investigated, in which a man had murdered his wife and got eighteen months for manslaughter. It was a mirror-image of Lindsay's present situation. That did get me thinking. I asked Mo to find out more about Dawn – Lindsay had said she'd been a school teacher. Mo said she'd go down to the school and interview the headmistress. We then arranged to meet up later in the afternoon, outside Dawn's mother's house.

Before going into the house to meet Dawn's family, Mo and I chatted in my car. The headmistress had told Mo that Dawn wasn't the type to have an affair – she just didn't have the time. She was too busy running around, doing her job and looking after her husband and kids, whom she adored. The head had admitted that Dawn had been particularly stressed the previous term, but had not confided in her. The dead woman's only real confidant had been her sister Gayle. We talked to Gayle inside the house. She didn't tell us much, other than to confirm what the school head had already told us. She was extremely distressed by her sister's death – all the time we spoke with her she was crying and shaking like a leaf. Mo and I decided it would be kinder if we left and visited her again another day.

The following day I made a trip to Lindsay's house to see whether I could pick up any new ideas from a second visit. In his bedroom everything was neat and tidy. Clean, as well. Obviously Dawn's depression didn't interfere with her household chores. I picked up a photo of their two kids which was sitting on the dresser. Lindsay had put in a request for a photograph of his children. I didn't see why the man should suffer any more than he had already. I made a mental note to drive by the station later on in the day to deliver the picture.

In one of the kid's bedrooms I saw a cut-out of a large Valentine Day's heart. I got to thinking about the dinner with the Kings that had been postponed three times – Lindsay had told us during his interview that one of them had been planned for Valentine's Day. I also remembered from my first visit that Dawn had kept a kitchen calendar. I had noticed it when Mo, Harry and I were talking in the kitchen on the night of the murder.

I shot downstairs. I was right – Dawn did have a kitchen calendar, and in it were written, in a very careful and organised manner, all the dates which were important to her – the kids' dental appointments, Scout evenings, her keep-fit classes. I flipped through the calendar until my finger was resting against February 14th. Nothing. No note of any dinner-party with the Kings. Lindsay had told us that after he had cancelled that first meal, a rematch was planned for the week following. February 21st – still no mention of a dinner date in Dawn's calendar. March 7th, the night of the murder, the night Lindsay had to cancel yet another meal at the Kings – absolutely nothing in Dawn's calendar.

At this point I stopped believing in anything Lindsay had told me during the interview. All my sympathy evaporated. Mo had been right. He'd been lying to us, and I now wanted him for murder – not manslaughter. However, time was not on my side. I had to charge him formally that day, or ask for an extension. I thought I'd give the extension a go.

I drove around to Fleet Road with the photograph in my jacket pocket. The last thing I wanted to happen now was for Lindsay to think I had something on him and so refuse my request for an extension. I played him at his own game – acting concerned, giving him the photo of his kids, and oh, by the way, I'd like a twelve-hour extension as I haven't been able to talk to your GP about Dawn's health. He took my story at face value – just as he was supposed to. Just as I had accepted his.

It was now evening, but I was so excited I rushed round to Mo's flat. I wanted her to know that I was with her and that together we'd get Lindsay. I wanted to tell her about my discovery in the house that morning, as well. I even brought a bottle of decent Spanish red to share with her. It was all hugely embarrassing. I didn't even know that Mo had a boyfriend, let alone that she was living with him. To be truthful, I had begun to suspect that she didn't like men very much anyway. Actually that wasn't a brilliant deduction – but it was something Jenny had said to me a few months back. Anyway, I'd obviously arrived at a bad moment. Mo was in a towel and – Richard? – was cooking dinner for two. I should have left but no, I began to tell Mo about the calendar in the kitchen and the blanks it contained. I didn't stop talking because Mo seemed eager to hear more; she was delighted I'd come round to her way of thinking. During all this time Richard was silent. When I paused for breath he told Mo he was about to be made redundant from his job at a design agency. Sudden silence filled the living room. I made my apologies and retreated. It was only when I got to my car that I realised I was still clutching the bottle of red wine.

The next day I was sitting at my desk when Mo came rushing in. I was surprised to see her – I thought she'd be late. She was very excited. She had just discovered that the words Lindsay had used in his confession were almost identical to a confession made to him five years earlier in one of his previous cases by the man who had murdered his wife. If Lindsay had gone to all the trouble of setting up a replay of an old manslaughter case as part of a plan to murder his wife, he had to have a pretty strong motive. We had less than six hours to find out – after that I had to charge him, and we needed to have enough evidence of intent to make a murder charge stick. Once he was charged with murder, he would clam up and our main source of information – Lindsay himself – would be lost to us.

Affairs were always a good starting point; they had got me into enough trouble, after all. Mo and I decided to check up on any out-of-town jobs Lindsay had undertaken over the past six months, as they were the best places for affairs to flourish. We came up trumps. Lindsay had been in Henley less than two months back. Mo and I took a little trip up there to see what we could find. I broke the speed limit driving there. We were really up against it now.

We visited the hotel in which Lindsay had stayed during the course of his investigation. We were in luck. The hotelier remembered a Mr and Mrs Lindsay checking in because he had been investigating a local robbery in which a policeman had been killed. We showed him a photograph of Dawn. He wasn't sure if that had been the woman Lindsay was with, but the maid who had cleaned their rooms was. Mo and I had drawn a blank. We headed back down to London. We only had four hours left. We decided to try Dawn's sister again.

Gayle was at her mother's, looking after Lindsay's children, who clearly adored her. Dawn's mother seemed a strong and capable woman, so we asked her about Dawn's relationship with Lindsay. She told us they had been childhood sweethearts, and Dawn had become increasingly dependent on Lindsay after the death of her father. Lindsay, in turn, had been wonderful with the family, helping both Dawn and Gayle through that difficult time. All this time Gayle was shaking; she was in such a state that she couldn't even hold a cup; tea was sloshing all over the saucer. I caught Mo's eye. I asked if I could ask her a few questions in a room away from her mother.

I quizzed her about the baby-sitting arrangements with Dawn. I was told that Dawn had been so protective of the children that, if she was going out with her husband, she wouldn't think of using any sitter other than Gayle. However, Dawn hadn't been in touch with her on the evening of the planned dinner with the Kings – the evening of her murder. Gayle warmed to her theme. Dawn was such a good mother that she'd never leave the children overnight. That's why she never went away with Lindsay on business trips. Henley. The maid had identified Dawn from a photo: a thin blonde woman. I looked at her sister sitting across from me. Thin and blonde. It was then that what had gone on in Henley clicked.

When confronted, Gayle cracked. She told me that some six months back Lindsay and she had made love in her hall after he had driven her back from a night of baby-sitting. She was smitten by Lindsay – but she knew how much he loved Dawn. They both did. He would never kill her, she told me. Gayle believed her sister had been killed by accident. Now I knew better. I asked Gayle to come with me to Fleet Road Police Station to make a statement.

When we arrived at the nick, I warned the custody sergeant not to let on to Lindsay that Gayle had been brought in. Neither Mo nor I thought she was an accomplice, but she had provided Lindsay's motive for killing Dawn. He loved Gayle, Gayle would get custody of the kids while he was serving his sentence, and in time she would forgive him for the terrible accident which had left her sister dead. Gayle had always loved Lindsay, we'd been told by her mother. And he was going to get it all. Gayle and his two kids.

We only had a couple of hours left in which to charge him formally. I told Mo to get a statement out of Gayle within fifty minutes, while I would read the forensic report which Harry had just brought in. Dawn's post-mortem showed that death was by strangulation. Her alcohol levels were low – too low for someone who had been drinking as heavily as Lindsay had alleged. Most interesting of all, a Dutch cap was found inside her vagina, suggesting that she had been expecting to have sex at some point in the evening. This didn't tie in with the story Lindsay had been telling us. The presence of a Dutch cap suggested that Dawn had been anticipating sex – not a row, not a fight, and certainly not death at the hands of her husband. Harry then brought me back down to earth, however. All the evidence we had was circumstantial. It wouldn't convince a jury that Lindsey was guilty of premeditated murder. Our only hope was that he would admit to the charges we were going to present him with. We needed a confession. Mo and I walked into the interview room. Lindsay was already there, waiting for us.

I started off by asking him a list of general questions – about his financial situation, his work, and then about sex. I led him into it gently, asking him when he had last made love to his wife. He told me it was over two weeks back. I then asked him about contraception. He replied slowly, carefully. He realised that we were on to something; I could see it in his expression. I tried to divert him by asking about Dawn's drinking habits. His reply was different from the one he had given us in the first interview, when he had inferred that she had been drinking heavily. He told us this time that she had stopped drinking – which was why she had been so tense. My mind was racing. Had Dawn been so tense that she didn't leave her seat by the TV all evening, as Lindsay had previously suggested? Not even to go to the loo? Not even to go upstairs to insert her Dutch cap? I stored that all away in my head, hoping that I could use it within the next few minutes to throw Lindsay off guard.

I quizzed him about Gayle. It was then that he realised we knew. I asked him about his relationship with her – and reminded him of the occasion when an old boyfriend of hers had brought her home on a motorbike and Lindsay had threatened to break his legs.

Lindsay's answer was 'No comment'. We had ten minutes left in which to drag a confession out of him.

I reverted back to Dawn and the missing dates on her wall calendar. Lindsay's answer, telling us she was forgetful, must have sounded pretty unconvincing even to him. Five minutes left. I homed in on the murder, and read him the confession of Richard Sabatowski, the man Lindsay had arrested five years earlier for the murder of his wife. He offered no comment as to why his and Sabatowski's confessions should be identical.

I then offered to read him Gayle's statement, made earlier that day, in which she had admitted that they were lovers, and were having an affair. No comment.

Finally, I played the trump card. I told him about the Dutch cap. The last evening of Dawn Lindsay's life couldn't have been as chilly and awful as he made out. When he had got in from work he put the kids to bed and made her dinner. Dawn had been thrilled by his kindness. She wanted to make love to him that night. She went upstairs to her bedroom and inserted her Dutch cap – half an hour before he murdered her.

Yours truly.

With Sue who, for once in her life, is smiling.

Jenny looking as
lovely as ever.

Me and Jenny.
These photos
were taken
shortly
before her
death.

Mo and Harry trawling through evidence
during my first case at CIB.

The Coverdale Road saga ended in a full-scale
riot; it was only thanks to that bastard Jamison
that we escaped from this hell hole.

Harry in
typically
relaxed pose.

And me.

Mo and I en route to see an informant.

For some reason,
Harry insisted
that the
receptionist here
took our picture.

Harry and
Deakin looking
very solemn.
We were working
on the Beckett
Park case when
this was taken
and tensions
were running
high.

Sue took this photo just before she left me.

Harry and I dressed up to the nines. Despite appearances,
there was to be no ballroom dancing for Harry that night.

With Huxtable and Deakin.

With Deakin; we're
not the best of
friends nowadays.

Flanked by my bosses: little did I know
when this was taken that I'd be responsible
for arresting one of them weeks later.

Us shortly after we
collared Deakin.

Huxtable not long
after Deakin's
arrest.

Harry looking exhausted. I didn't realise it at the time but Harry had been holding down two jobs.

This was taken just after I met Angela Berridge.

Our time had run out. We didn't have sufficient evidence to prove that the murder was premeditated, and Lindsay had confessed to nothing. I had to lead Mo out of the room, she was crying so hard.

So the bastard went down for manslaughter. I know he's a murderer – cold-blooded, calculating, unfeeling – but I also know why he murdered his wife. He wanted Gayle and a cosy life with her and the kids. He must realise by now that he'll never get that; Gayle must have enough doubts about the death of her sister not to want to take a chance on him. I have ruined everything for which he laid such meticulous plans. He's killed once, he could certainly kill again. The death threats may just be his way of letting me know that when he gets out of jail, he'll be coming for me.

Suspect Dossier file No.: 12
Subjects: DETECTIVE SUPERINTENDENT GARY SLATER & BETTY COOGAN

Gary Slater was like an urban commando who allowed only one form of justice into his life – his own. He had absolutely no respect for anybody – not for the criminals down on his patch at the Cornhill Estate, not for the other police officers he came into contact with, and certainly not for me. From the very beginning he let me know what he felt for police officers in suits, and that was utter contempt. His go-it-alone attitude didn't help him, though. In fact, it finished his career. He must be an extremely bitter man.

I first ran into Slater when I investigated the shooting on Harris Street. There had been a hold-up on an off-licence; two armed robbers who were out of their heads on crack had beaten up the Asian owner and had shot his wife in the arm. Almost instantly an Armed Response vehicle was on the scene, the coppers surrounding the off-licence, shouting 'Armed Police!'. In the confusion that followed, one of the robbers loosed off a couple of rounds, and the next thing that happened was that he was shot dead. His mate got away.

Graves apprised me of the situation. I had been working late in my office, trying to clear my desk of some paperwork. When I paused to look out of the window I saw that it was dark outside. It was time to go home. Then Graves walked in to tell me of the Harris Street incident. By then I had begun to suspect that Graves never actually went home. He could be found at any time, day or night, somewhere in the offices of CIB. I don't believe he even stopped working long enough to have a crap. Which was probably why the man was so full of shit.

Graves told me to get down to Harris Street. Two CID officers had asked for Armed-Response support as they had been tipped off about the off-licence hold up. I was to go down and interview everybody concerned. Before leaving the office I rang Harry and Mo.

When I got down to the scene of the shooting the place was in uproar – police, sirens and flashing blue lights everywhere. The first man I spoke to was PC Duskin from the Armed Response Unit. He told me that all the men in the van were armed with rifles. They'd been called out to Harris Street at 5:50 pm, to assist two local CID officers whose names I took down – Slater and Green. Duskin then told me that he'd shot the black robber. He was visibly upset and told me he had had no choice – the man had been out of his head on something and had been running around, waving his gun. He'd already shot the woman in the off-licence. He was a danger to the public and the police officers present, and he had to be stopped. At that moment Harry and Mo arrived so I left them to continue the interview with Duskin. I wanted to talk to the CID officer who had asked for armed assistance.

I saw DS Slater standing a couple of yards away from the dead man. Rain was pouring down on him. He looked streetwise and hard, but in spite of that he seemed ill at ease. He actually looked exactly like an undercover detective who was trying not to be noticed. His clothes were scruffy but well cut, and his wiry red hair was tied back in a pony tail. He stood out a mile. I went over to him and introduced myself. Slater told me his version of the events. Earlier that day his snout had rung him to say Chip Coogan – the man now lying dead on the pavement – had been waving a gun around, saying that he was going to do a blag on the off-licence in Harris Street. That call had come to Slater at 5:40 and he had rung his boss immediately. He supposed it had been his boss who then asked for armed support; it certainly hadn't been him. When he and his partner, Green, had arrived at the off-licence, the boys with the guns had beaten them to it. I asked him whether he or Green had been armed. It was then that I got a glimpse of his real character. He told me that he wished he had been.

He wished it had been him who had shot Chip Coogan dead. He would rather have kept the whole incident 'in the family'. When I asked him what he meant, he told me that he hadn't wanted any intervention from the Armed Response Unit. He was pissed off that they had 'had all the fun', as he put it. He was cocky, and he was getting right up my nose. Just then Harry walked up to me to say that all the lads in the Armed Response call-out were clean. They had followed correct police procedure and had shot Coogan only after they had identified themselves as armed police and he had fired upon them. There were quite a few witnesses who could support their story.

The police vehicles and ambulances had by now dispersed, but already a crowd had begun to gather outside the off-licence, laying down wreaths and flowers on the spot where Coogan had been killed. I saw an elderly black woman being led away from the off-licence – she was weeping. Obviously Coogan's mother. I decided it was time to go home.

In the office the next day I received the results of Coogan's autopsy. It showed that he had cocaine in his bloodstream and powder on his fingers. It confirmed that he had been out of his head on crack when the police had shot him. I thought that that would be the end of the case, but then Graves came into my office and I knew I wasn't through yet. He told me the Asian woman from the off-licence who had been shot was in a 'comfortable' condition. I remember Graves being so relieved – relieved that she had been Asian, so that the police shooting couldn't be turned into a racial incident. The man was all heart. He then told me that Coogan's family had requested a meeting with the Police Complaints Authority and Graves wanted me to go along with its representative, George McKenzie. I couldn't believe Graves was asking me to do that, and told him so. I knew Coogan's family would tell me to piss off, or worse. However, Graves wouldn't listen to me – on principle, as much as anything else.

George McKenzie and I arranged to meet up with Coogan's family at the local Black Youth Centre. I had taken Mo along with me – for support. I suspected that we were going to be given a hard time. At the Youth Centre we were introduced to David Baron, the centre's co-ordinator. He then led us into his office, where Betty Coogan and her other son were waiting. On finding out who I was she refused to shake my hand, and accused my people of murdering her son. She then asked me to leave. I left. I had known that the meeting would turn out to be a waste of our time. Mo and I headed back to the office. End of case, I thought again.

A couple of days later I wandered into the office a bit later than usual, as I hadn't been able to find any clean socks and my shirt had been one of those which was almost impossible to iron. Harry looked up from whatever it was that he had been doing. He motioned with his pencil to Graves' office. Obviously Graves wanted to see me, sharpish. It hadn't been a good day on which to come in late, then.

George McKenzie was sitting in Graves's office. As soon as I got my coffee and sat down, they played me a tape which had been sent anonymously to the PCA first thing that morning. It was a tape of Coogan talking to two CID officers – Slater and Green. Up to that point I had actually forgotten about them; the Coogan incident was closed as far as I was concerned. But the tape instantly reopened the case. On it we heard Slater, Green and Coogan. They offered him some crack – and then a gun. My conversation with Slater came back to me. If Slater had given Coogan a gun then in effect he had set him up – and Slater had told me himself that he had wanted Coogan dead. Slater also obviously knew Coogan better than he had let on to me. I was going to get his balls over this. I went back to my office and arranged to interview him the following day.

My second interview with Slater didn't endear me to him any more than had the first. I asked him about Coogan, and Slater told me that he thought he was just another apeman from Cornhill Estate. He added that ever since the arrival of crack it was like a war-zone out there.

I played him the tape, and accused him of instigating the raid on the off-licence which had resulted in Coogan's death. Slater denied any involvement, saying that the conversation on the tape was just regular police business and that Coogan was a registered snout. Harry had checked up on Slater's snouts and Coogan wasn't on the list. Slater blamed that on incomplete paperwork. I then accused him of peddling drugs and running guns. Slater claimed that it was all just talk, getting down to the informant's level. He did it all the time. He then went straight to the top of my shit-list by telling me to go back to arranging pencils on my desk, and to leave the real police work to the grown-ups.

I felt like pounding him. Instead I went back to the office and told Graves that Slater and his partner should be suspended from duty because they were as dangerous as the criminals they were after. Graves agreed. So I had my revenge. That would show Slater what I thought about his 'rearranging pencils' crack.

Soon after their suspension I was summoned to Commander Sullivan's office. He wanted me to make sure that the allegations against Slater and Green were watertight; that their conversation with Coogan was genuine; that the tape wasn't a fake. I told him that our technical experts had the tape and they had confirmed that it was genuine, but truncated – which led me to believe that a full version must exist somewhere. Sullivan reacted to that. He wanted the original tape found before somebody went public with it and the newspapers got hold of the full story. But finding it was going to be an enormous task.

Three days later we still hadn't made any progress with tracking down the original tape. We had assumed that the conversation had been recorded on Coogan's Walkman. The section of the tape that we had was recorded on a brand-name cassette that was widely available, and it was never going to provide us with any leads. I decided to target the people who were closest to Coogan, on the off chance that he had slipped the full tape to one of them. They broke down into three groups – his family, the local community, and the local police. I warned Harry and Mo to tread carefully – all three groups were hostile to CIB.

Mo started off by trying to talk to Coogan's family again, and this time she had a degree of success. Betty Coogan still wasn't talking to us, but her son was. He told Mo he was a sergeant too – in the British Army. He went on to tell her that he hadn't been very close to Chip, but had been closer to their oldest brother, Michael, who had also joined the army. He'd been blown to pieces in Northern Ireland five years back. Their mother had never really recovered from the shock of losing her first son, and had subsequently spoilt Chip, her youngest.

Harry went to interview Green at home, to try and persuade him to bring his snout in for questioning – the snout who had alerted them to the fact that Coogan had a shooter. At first, Green didn't want to know. He and Slater felt they had been badly let down by the police force – they were fighting a war against crack and their bosses just didn't want to know. Harry then persuaded him it was in his best interests to allow us to talk to his informant. After all, prolonged suspension from a job meant the end of a career and loss of earnings. And Green had a young family to support and a cherished classic car to maintain. Green decided to co-operate.

We met Harvey Mannell, the snout, outside some lock-ups in South-East London. He arrived with Green, but we transferred him to the back of my car and then went for a drive. Mannell was a nervous, sweaty young black man who shook constantly. There was a sweetish smell coming from him and I guessed that he was a crack addict. At first he didn't make too much sense, but once he had calmed down and realised that we were not there to put him away, he told us what had happened on the day of Coogan's shooting. Earlier on that afternoon he and Chip had smoked a couple of rocks which they had bought. It was then that Coogan had pulled out his gun and said that he was going to do the off-licence – he needed more money for crack. Once Coogan had left Mannell's flat, Mannell had rung Slater. He had been supplying information to Slater and Green ever since they had caught him with a stone and had threatened to charge him with possession, as well as spreading the word that he was a grass. Mannell had had no choice but to become their snout. In return he received the occasional tenner and the occasional rock. Thus Slater and Green – if Mannell was to be believed – had paid their informants with drugs. We could do them both for that alone.

I told Mannell about the tape, and asked him who among Coogan's friends would have been the most likely recipient. Mannell gave the name of Coogan's girlfriend, Annette. He told us that she was a crackhead who would pork anything for a stone. We had to bring her in for questioning. Mannell told us the most likely place to find her would be outside the Sporting Life pub. She was there most nights, selling herself for some stones.

I knew that as CIB officers we couldn't just go storming into the Sporting Life, demanding to know the whereabouts of Annette. We had to approach the matter in an altogether more subtle way. My solution was brilliant. At 9pm Harry and I parked outside the Sporting Life, observing Mo, who had dressed up like a tart in high heels, stockings and a PVC mini-skirt. I hadn't really noticed before that she had really good legs – she'd probably wised up to me from the word go, which is why she only wore trouser suits into the office. As we had agreed earlier, Mo approached a group of prostitutes by the pub and made enquiries as to Annette's whereabouts.

However, the other girls weren't interested in helping out a rival who might take their trade; instead they turned on Mo. Harry and I blew our cover and rushed out of the car to save her skin. We were in the middle of an almighty scrap with whores, their pimps and the pub's usual punters when we were rescued by David Baron from the community centre. He hauled us out of the scrum with only a few minor bruises and scratches. I asked him about Annette Marsh. Baron just walked away. He may have saved our necks, but he wasn't going to do us any more favours. It was his community, after all.

Back at CIB, Graves was so horrified by Mo's cut cheek and black eye that he decided to give us as much help as we needed in finding Annette Marsh and the tape. In a debriefing meeting I instructed an entire squad of officers whom Graves had assigned to us to search the Cornhill, Angel and Jarnett Estates for Annette. I personally led a raid on a brothel-cum-crack den on the Cornhill estate. The place stank of booze, smoke and vomit, and half the people we stumbled over in the search weren't even on this planet. It was good to get out of that place into the 'fresh' city air. But by the end of the day we still hadn't found Annette or the tape. It was as if they had vanished into thin air.

Three days later I was just about giving up on the search when the door of my office was thrown open and David Baron burst in. He told me that Harvey Mannell had been murdered – and he thought he knew by whom. Annette and Coogan's accomplice, a white lad called Lloyd Manning, had decided to take revenge on Coogan's grass. They had tortured and killed Mannell, leaving his body cut in shreds in a stinking alley on the Cornhill Estate. This was too much for Baron. The last thing he needed was a couple of nutters running loose in his community. He told us we would find Annette in a squat down on the Jarnett Estate.

Annette Marsh screamed and kicked like a wildcat when we finally tracked her down. In my office I told her that she was going to be questioned about Mannell's murder, but not by me. I just wanted to know where the tape was. If Annette had known, she would have told me. She was eager to deal – but she knew nothing. All that effort and we'd drawn a blank. It was time to question Lloyd Manning, the youth Baron had told us about. However, before I went back to the Cornhill Estate to track him down, I was informed he had come to us. Not to CIB Division, but CID. Lloyd Manning had been arrested for pushing the suspended DS Gary Slater off a third-floor balcony down on the Cornhill Estate. It was my guess that Slater had been trying to find the original tape before we did.

Slater was lucky to be alive. He had crushed his right hip and leg in the fall. There was very little chance that when his suspension was lifted he would recover sufficiently to resume his duties on the street. The only police work he could look forward to was pushing paper around an office desk.

Once CID had finished interviewing Manning, he was passed on to me. I asked him for the tape. He denied ever having had it – he may have been Coogan's best mate but they had never really been all that close. He told me that the only person Chip Coogan really trusted was his mother. I remembered Betty Coogan – how much she hated us for having taken her boy from her; how bitter she was that the British Army had taken her other son. I knew then that Coogan had left the tape with her. In retrospect, it should have been obvious.

I rounded up Mo and was just getting into the car with her when Harry came running up. He had spent the morning with Green and Slater at the hospital where Slater was recovering. Green was so upset over his partner's injury that he had decided to tell Harry the truth. There was no point in keeping secrets if Slater was going to be invalided out of the force.

He told Harry that both of them had known Coogan. They had been following him for some months and had finally caught him coming out of the back of a pharmacy with a bagful of drugs and syringes. They had even taken photographs of him. They had then leant heavily on him because they wanted him to tell them the name of the major crack supplier who was feeding the estates. But they never gave Coogan a shooter. Green stuck to that story. The three of us – Harry, Mo and I – went over to Betty Coogan's flat. We wanted to hear what was on that tape. She wasn't there, but her son was, and we told him why we had come and what we wanted. He took us down to see his mother. She was working as an office cleaner, and froze when she saw us entering the room.

She gave me the tape without resistance – just resignation. Mo, Harry and I sat in the car and listened to it, from start to finish: the uncut version. By the end of it we were much wiser as to what had gone down between Slater, Green and Coogan. The two officers had been telling the truth. They'd been taking the piss out of Coogan – not only had they offered him a gun, but a Scud missile as well. They finished by telling him to dream on, because they'd never give him anything. Although aggressive and abusive, they had been straight. We, on the other hand, had screwed up. We drove in silence to the Sporting Life. Outside, it was business as usual. The whores, their pimps and the crack dealers were still there. Nothing had changed.

Slater ultimately left the force – he couldn't walk without the aid of a stick. He blamed CIB for his accident, and our investigation into his affairs meant that he never did find out who the crack supplier in his patch had been. As far as he was concerned, his life was over. He resigned from the police force soon after I closed the file on the Harris Street incident. He wasn't going to spend the rest of his career typing up other officers' reports. He must feel extremely bitter towards me, and I wouldn't blame him if he wanted revenge. Of course, another person who feels the same way about me is Betty Coogan. She'd lost two sons, and blamed the British establishment for their deaths. She had doctored the original tape to implicate Slater, and had used us as the instruments of her revenge. And she could now be sending me those poisonous letters, for they seem very much in keeping with her style. And I have the feeling that a mother's capacity for revenge is limitless.

Suspect Dossier file No.: 13
Subject: THE SCARECROW

My investigation into the break-in at the Crouch End Territorial Army Centre marked a turning point in my career and in my life. It was there I had my first real dealings with MI5; it was only when the investigation was closed that I realised why everybody else on the force called them 'the Spooks'. They were very scary; they were very, very powerful; and they could disappear whenever they chose to.

It was also during this investigation that I first met Angela Berridge, although I didn't trust her, or even like her at first. It's funny how first impressions can be so misleading. I didn't have an inkling then of what a profound impact she'd have on my life. And finally, it was during this investigation that I began to smoke again – probably more heavily than ever before. Dealing with MI5 does that to you: they destroy your confidence in your ability to do a job, and then they shoot your nerves to pieces.

It was last summer that Mo, Harry and I were summoned to Crouch End TA Centre to investigate a shooting there. We heard the incident reported on the car radio as we drove in – it was the top news item. However, the news people had only got hold of half the story. It was true that an as-yet-unidentified man had been shot by armed police officers in the drill hall but what they didn't report was that the officer who had done the shooting was a member of the Special Branch, and had been staking out the TA Centre with his partner.

During their routine observation, they had seen a Mercury van pull up outside, and three men get out and, with the aid of a ladder, climb over the wall of the TA Centre. The Special Branch officers leapt into action – this was a pretty definite unofficial entry, and the armoury in the Centre housed a huge stockpile of firearms and ammunition. One of the officers on surveillance, an Inspector Pollock, had then rung his boss to report the incident and to ask for permission to draw arms. He also asked for armed support and for uniformed officers to seal the street – he wanted to contain the intruders inside the TA Centre. Within minutes the operation was under way. The first man to be apprehended was the look-out, who was waiting by the van. The Special Branch officers together with the armed police then entered the building. In the drill hall, by the armoury, they heard a noise. Bursting through the doors they had identified themselves as armed police. An intruder was at the door of the armoury – he turned, gun in hand. Pollock, the Special Branch officer, had had no choice. He shot him dead. And that's when we were called in.

As we approached the TA Centre we could see it was surrounded by both military and Metropolitan police – it looked like Fort Knox, or a maximum-security prison on full alert. I showed my ID to the army officer guarding the entrance, telling him we were CIB and that we were investigating the incident. He wasn't impressed. He told me that the Army's Special Investigations Branch was dealing with it already, and that all the police officers involved had been taken to Crouch End Police Station. I swore and reversed my car. Crouch End station was only five minutes up the road. Once there we were introduced to Chief Superintendent Newell. He confirmed that it had been Pollock who had discharged the weapon, and that the intruder had been killed outright with two bullet wounds in his chest. Unfortunately, the intruder hadn't exactly been armed, as Special Branch had thought. He died with a cordless drill in his hand.

Newell led us through to the canteen, where all the officers involved in the shooting had been ordered to remain. I recognised Pollock instantly; he was the young officer sitting by himself, staring sightlessly into his cup of tea. He looked devastated. I told Mo and Harry to sort out the officers – to take statements from everybody, including Pollock. I left with Newell to go down to the cells, which was where they had put the three intruders. On the way down Newell informed me that the three men weren't saying a word, other than that they were MI5.

Newell unlocked the cell door and I went in. I was confronted by three casually dressed men who didn't seem to be particularly bothered at having been locked up. I asked them to give me witness statements of the shooting. One of them – the pre-elected spokesman, I guessed – replied they were not authorised to do so. I said we'd start at the beginning – I wanted their names, ranks and numbers. Again, I was met with a wall of silence. I couldn't believe these guys. They wouldn't tell me anything; they just sat there smirking, as if being with MI5 absolved them of any responsibility or respect for authority. I lost my rag, told them I was charging them with breaking and entering, and stalked out of the cell. Once outside, Newell and I had a chat. Neither of us could believe those men were real. Newell told me that while I was conducting my fruitless interviews in the cells, he had had a call from the Home Office; they were sending a representative over to sort out the situation. I went back to the canteen to see how Harry and Mo were doing with the other officers. The three men had put me into such a filthy mood that I asked Harry for his fags. He passed them over without comment – he knew I was having a hard time, but he did that recommend I take my patch off before I lit my first one. He didn't want to see me going down with nicotine poisoning just before the arrival of the Home Office man.

I went back down to the reception desk, where I had been told that the Home Office official was waiting. He looked extremely unprepossessing – incredibly shabby and wrinkled, both his clothes and his skinny body. He did have the most astonishing piercing blue eyes, however, which seemed to hold an expression of mockery or contempt. Maybe I was just being fanciful, but that was what it seemed like to me. He introduced himself to me – or rather, he didn't. He just said that he was a director from 'A' Branch in MI5 and he had come to collect 'his three bods', as he put it. I was buggered if I was going to let him.

I asked him what authority he had and what authority did his three men have to be in the TA Centre in the first place. The man just handed me a piece of Home Office letterhead with a few lines of garbage printed on it. I was unimpressed. He told me not to be silly – and then very politely threatened me: I didn't know what I was doing he said – an MI5 Director had the same rank as a Police Commander. I really didn't like his patronising manner.

Since he wouldn't tell me who he was (I'd already christened him 'Scarecrow' in my mind) but did claim responsibility for the three men in the cells, I decided to arrest him, too. I told him I was doing him for conspiracy to burgle, then I left the room as he pulled out his mobile phone. I was just within earshot when I heard him make his call. He was telling someone that he was having trouble with 'the Plod'. For that alone, I was 73 determined to get him. I was so unimpressed by the MI5 people I had met in the course of the afternoon that I decided to give Special Branch all the help and support I could. I went back to the canteen and had a brief word with Pollock, advising him off the record to say nothing to anybody. I hadn't liked MI5's evasive manner, and I didn't want to see anyone get fitted up for something they hadn't done.

I told Pollock to go home, thinking I might just do the same myself. However, the afternoon's fun hadn't even begun. Newell came into the canteen and told the remaining officers still there to get out. He then asked me to help him rearrange some chairs in a circle. I was then shocked to see the door to the canteen open and some extremely heavyweight top brass enter the room, accompanied by several men in grey suits, the Scarecrow, and my boss, Commander Graham Sullivan.

Everybody sat down, and one of the suits introduced himself as Thomas Wenleigh, the Deputy Under-Secretary at the Home Office. He immediately took charge, informing everyone present that he was there to scrape up the shit before it hit the fan. He then asked everyone in the room to identify themselves. I became even more concerned when the roll-call sounded off; I wanted to know what the hell was going on. Rear-Admiral Sir Timothy Vaughan Taylor, Chairman of the PCA; my boss at CIB; Deputy Assistant Commissioner John Gollap, head of Special Branch; Newell; myself; Major Weatherill from Army Intelligence and Security Staff; Angela Berridge from the Home Office; and two senior officers from MI5, one of whom was the Scarecrow. He just smiled at me. He knew I'd never find out his identity.

The meeting began in an extremely unimpressive way. I was asked to relate the events leading up to the shooting. I lit a cigarette and started – but was stopped by Wenleigh, who alerted me to the dangers of passive smoking. I was gobsmacked – all these heavies from MI5 and the Home Office, and we were going to have a vote as to whether the meeting should be a non-smoking one. I'm delighted to report that the smokers won the day. All the senior police officers came out in support of me and lit up. I had carried the first motion.

Puffing on my fag, I informed the meeting that I couldn't tell them what was going on as I didn't know myself – at least half the people involved in the incident weren't authorised to talk to me. Second round to me as well. I was beginning to enjoy myself. I did tell them the sequence of events leading up to the shooting incident, but I then broke off, as I didn't know the ID of the dead man. The Scarecrow spoke up. He told the meeting that the dead man had not been MI5. I didn't – couldn't – believe him.

The whole investigation was becoming increasingly more complicated by the minute. I wanted out, but I wasn't going to get my wish. Wenleigh gave me a pep talk, telling me that because I was doing such a thorough job, he wanted me to continue investigating the case. I had to find out the identity of the dead man and question all the police officers involved, but I wouldn't have direct access to any MI5 personnel. By the sound of things, Wenleigh wanted both to have his cake and eat it. Another person who didn't like Wenleigh's proposal was DAC John Gollap of Special Branch. He pointed out that Special Branch officers were subject to disciplinary action, even imprisonment, if they stepped out of line, while MI5 officers, doing much the same kind of job, could simply just 'disappear'.

74   I could tell that this investigation was rapidly turning into a minefield of rivalries,

jealousies and one-upmanship. Wenleigh agreed with Gollap. He said he didn't want a whitewash or a Whitehall cover-up, so I would be working on the police side of things while Angela Berridge would deal with MI5. We would then work together with 'full and frank co-operation'. I couldn't see this, myself, and I'm sure Angela Berridge must have been thinking the same thing. Wenleigh wound up the meeting. He emphasised that he wanted only those present in the room to be involved, and said that once Berridge and I had come to him with our findings, he would then decide how to proceed further. Absolutely nobody was to talk to the press; he didn't want any leaks. The meeting in the canteen finished when the kitchen hatch was rolled back and a large black woman asked us if we were staying for lunch. So much for top-level security then.

Sullivan and I left the building with a fuming DAC Gollap, who was complaining of an escalating 'us-against-them' situation with MI5. I listened with interest. It would seem that the rivalry between Special Branch and MI5 had grown ever since the end of the Cold War, when MI5 had no more spies to chase. They now wanted to go after drug dealers, terrorists, organised crime – all the people, in fact, that Special Branch were after. Gollap told Sullivan and me that he wouldn't have his men made into scapegoats; MI5 had no right to be at the TA Centre without Special Branch's knowledge. Before he left us, he threatened to have my bollocks if my investigations showed Special Branch in a bad light.

In the police car park I passed Angela Berridge, who was just getting into her car. I said I'd meet her in the drill hall, at the site of the shooting. The Military Police had been in touch with Crouch End station, to say that we could now have access to the building.

As I left the car park I passed Gollap giving an impromptu speech outside the police station to the journalists who had gathered there. He was telling them that Special Branch was carrying out the investigation with full Home Office support. Between the lines, however, he was inferring that MI5 was involved in order to start protecting himself and his officers from any dirty tricks the spooks might pull. Scanning the crowd of journalists, I caught a momentary glimpse of long dark hair tied back in a ponytail. I wondered what Molly Cope was doing with herself these days.

I met up with Harry in the drill hall of the TA Centre. He'd been looking at the bagged-up forensic evidence when I arrived, and showed me an ordinary brick – except that when he flipped it over it was packed with transistors and wires. Then he showed me other microphones and transmitters; Harry had done his stint at Special Branch and knew all about bugging devices – almost. I picked up two small clips of metal and asked him what they were, but he had to admit that he didn't know. Even so, it was clear that MI5 had been setting up bugs in the armoury when they had been interrupted by Special Branch.

We looked up when we heard Angela Berridge's heels click over the highly polished floor of the drill hall. I introduced her to Harry and really tried hard to be nice. The atmosphere remained strained. She suggested that I outline what our procedure should be – she was obviously trying hard to be nice, too. I made a list of suggestions. First, we had to find out why MI5 hadn't informed Special Branch of the bugging operation. Secondly, we had to establish that Inspector Pollock's actions had been justified – both the shooting of the intruder and the calling-in of the armed police officers. Thirdly, we had to find out the identity of the dead man. At this point Harry chipped in, telling us that the dead man was a Jack Edmonds. I gaped at him until he put me out of my misery – he had found the 75 dead man's wallet in amongst all the bagged-up forensic evidence. However, it still left us with the question of who Edmonds was and what he was doing in the TA Centre in the first place. I also had one really important question left for Angela Berridge: why was MI5 trying to bug the armoury? She did help us out on that one, telling us that MI5 had reason to suspect a TA soldier from Crouch End – a Corporal Hodges – of being in contact with members of a well-known terrorist organisation. Harry and I decided that the next step would be to interview Hodges, and Harry went off to organise it. Just before she left, Angela gave me her home number, in case of an emergency; she added that she hoped this was going to be the beginning of a long and fruitful partnership.

A few minutes later I joined Harry in the mess of the TA Centre, where he was talking to Captain Goods. Michael John David Hodges was being picked up by Crouch End police on his instructions. Before leaving for CIB I asked Captain Goods, one of the very few people who had seen the body before it had been taken away, whether he had known the dead man. Goods denied having ever seen the man – he hadn't been a regular maintenance man. The mystery surrounding Jack Edmonds deepened.

Back at CIB Mo collared me to tell me that Edmonds had been a painter/decorator. In the past he had worked for the Ministry of Transport, and before that for a private firm. At least now we knew that he wasn't with the TA and he wasn't with MI5. I asked Mo to see what she could do about finding out who he really was – Mo was good at digging. As I walked into my office the phone rang. Talk of the Devil – it was Molly Cope. Well, I had been thinking about her, anyway. As ever, she quizzed me about my work, but by this time I had learnt my lesson. I told her nothing, and suggested dinner instead, which she accepted. It was good to see her again. She looked just as lovely as ever, though she told me she was now older and wiser. I told her about Sue, she told me she was still at the *Guardian*. Strangely, neither of us had the urge to leap into bed with the other. Maybe we really were too old and too tired; on the other hand, maybe we had just become really good friends.

When I turned up at the office the next day, Sullivan was already at my desk, reading the *Telegraph*. He showed me an article on page 2 which carried all Jack Edmonds's details. He was quite convinced that it had been MI5 which had leaked the information to the press; like Gollap, he was sure the spooks were out to shaft Special Branch. Equally, he found it interesting that MI5 had so many details on the dead man. As he told me, MI5, the House of Commons, the Home Office and the newspaper editors had all been fiddling with each other in their prep school dorms long before they were let loose on the rest of us. I just stared at my boss, beginning to see him in a totally new light. I really liked the man – he had my sense of humour. Before we got too pally and I slapped him on the back or did something equally unforgivable like that, he had reverted to Commander mode. He told me to go out and prove that Edmonds had been with MI5. It was a tough order to fill.

I went to get a coffee, and got back to my office to find Angela Berridge waiting outside. I'd had enough of her sneaking MI5 ways, so I invited her in and suggested to her that MI5 had known Edmonds was in the building. She denied that that was the case, but I was determined to give her a hard time. I said I thought it strange that MI5 had had no knowledge of him, bearing in mind that they had entered the armoury through the door by which Edmonds had been working – and had been shot through. She ignored my accusations, telling me that Special Branch hadn't been informed of the operation because MI5 were distrustful of Special Branch security. Sullivan had been hovering outside my office for just long enough to catch that last comment. He stormed in, incredulous. In his hand he carried a fax from Gollap, which had originally been sent to MI5 some months back. The fax contained details of Operation Septimus, an ongoing series of random surveillance operations designed to help Special Branch keep an eye on sensitive installations, such as Territorial Army centres. Septimus was a rolling surveillance which had been going on for months; years even. MI5 had known about it – and they could have checked with Special Branch beforehand to find out whether the Crouch End TA Centre was being watched that week. I'll give this much to Angela Berridge, her face gave nothing away, although I'm sure Sullivan's information must have been a real kick in the stomach.

The awkward atmosphere in my office was broken by Harry, who wandered in and told me that Hodges had been picked up and was now at Crouch End nick, waiting for us to interview him. We left immediately.

Hodges was a good-looking young bloke who seemed utterly baffled by his arrest. I started by confirming that his name was Michael John David Hodges. I then asked him whether he was a corporal in the 3rd Battalion, North Middlesex Regiment. He said no. I checked my notes – asked him his date of birth and the name of the school he had gone to. His answers checked with the information on my notepad, but he maintained that he was an industrial plumber who had never been in the army. Out of the corner of my eye I could see Harry trying hard not to grin, but I wasn't as amused as he was. I asked Captain Goods to come in. He'd been waiting outside the interview room until I'd finished with Hodges, as the TA had a few questions to ask him back at the Centre. Goods took one look at the man in the interview room and said it wasn't his Hodges. We let the man go – we had to, since he was perfectly innocent. What it did mean was that the TA's Corporal Hodges had been an impostor who had assumed the identity of Michael John David Hodges, industrial plumber.

The three of us – Goods, Harry and me – drove back to the TA Centre. I asked Goods about the fake Hodges. Apparently he had been a good soldier and a nice bloke. Goods had liked him, and had had high hopes for him. He told me Hodges had been a natural with weapons and was the Centre's storeman. As such, he had had access to Milan anti-tank missiles and scores of SA80 rifles. I hadn't realised until then that Crouch End TA Centre carried enough hardware to start a sizeable war. And it was extremely worrying that none of the TA personnel knew who Hodges was.

Harry and I met up with Mo in the drill hall, where she and a CIB boffin were examining the hinges on the armoury door. Just as we arrived the boffin removed from the door hinge a tiny detector which, he told us, would have sent out a signal whenever the door was opened. He guessed that Edmonds hadn't actually fitted the bug himself but was 'papering the cracks' to disguise any signs of tampering with the door. That's where his painting and decorating skills had been employed – he had been MI5's tidying-up man. The boffin went on to identify the two small clips which had baffled Harry as homing devices. It would seem that MI5 intended to bug the weapons in the armoury in the knowledge that they were about to be stolen, so that they could then track them to their final destination.

I'd had enough of MI5's manoeuvering, double-dealing, and witholding of information.

When I got back to my office I shut the door and made a phone call to Molly Cope, telling her – off the record – that Edmonds had been working for MI5.

Later in the day I was visited by Angela Berridge again. I determined to be casual with her, and told her that I knew Edmonds had been working with MI5. I also told her that I suspected the fake Hodges of being an IRA sympathiser – or of working with MI5. Either way, I believed Special Branch to be clean. She disagreed with me, and produced some black-and-white photographs out of her handbag. As I went through them she told me they had been taken twenty minutes after I had told Pollock to go home and get some rest. On leaving Couch End nick he hadn't gone home, but had gone to the house where 'Hodges' lived. She then produced more photos, which showed Pollock and 'Hodges' in a Kilburn pub, two weeks prior to the incident. The last photographs showed Hodges with a man called Demager, a well-known Irish terrorist who had served eight years for knee-capping. Just before Angela Berridge left she gave me a tape. On it was a conversation between Pollock and 'Hodges' in which they discussed the sale of arms to terrorists. They were talking about hundreds of thousands of pounds' worth of merchandise. I didn't like what was happening – I felt I was nothing but a puppet and MI5 were pulling my strings. I instructed Harry to get in touch with Pollock. We were going to interview him again.

Next morning Mo picked me up. She waved a *Guardian* in my face. The front page carried the story of Edmonds having worked for MI5. No journalist's name was credited to the story, but I think Mo knew. At Crouch End Police Station we met up with Harry, who'd been up for most of the night, going through Pollock's files and notebooks. He looked knackered, but it had proved a pointless exercise. He had not found a single reference to 'Hodges', nor had Pollock discussed 'Hodges' with his superior – Harry had rung in to check. Harry also told me that Wenleigh had rung the office when I wasn't there: both Angela Berridge and I were summoned to a meeting at 11am at his offices that day. My planned interview with Pollock would have to be brief. I asked him about 'Hodges' and what he knew about him. Pollock informed us that he had met him eighteen months ago at a squash tournament. They had got on well from the start. Six weeks ago 'Hodges' had rung Pollock, and he had said he was scared. He explained that he was a corporal in the TA with access to weapons, and that a man had got in touch with him and had indicated he was willing to buy some weapons from him. 'Hodges' didn't know what to do – the man had told him that he had another contact at the same TA Centre, which must have been true as he could describe the layout of the building perfectly. This had made 'Hodges' unwilling to inform his superiors; indeed, he now suspected them. Pollock suggested that they string the man along until they gathered enough information to nab him. I asked Pollock why he hadn't made any notes in his files, and he told us that he had; all dealings with 'Hodges' had been under the code name 'Jonah'. Harry went out to check, and he Pollock continued talking to me. He said that he had even received £2,000 as a down-payment from the would-be buyers, and he had deposited the money in the safe at South Hill Park nick in an envelope marked 'Retrieved Stolen Goods'. I'd heard enough to believe Pollock to be straight. At 9.14 am I suspended the interview because I wanted to talk informally to him.

I explained that the shooting incident had become incidental, and that this whole affair now looked like a battle between MI5 and Special Branch, and added that I believed

MI5 had set him up in order to discredit Special Branch. I told him about the tape; how ambiguous it had sounded, and how it could be used to work either to MI5's or to Special Branch's advantage.

Pollock then said something which straightened things up in my mind, for I then knew what we were up against. He told me that the only way MI5 could have got a recording of that conversation was if they had bugged his phone at Special Branch. 'Hodges' had only ever rung him at the office, and always from a call-box. I went along to the Home Office meeting more certain than I had ever been about what was going on in the investigation. And I really didn't like what was happening.

Although I arrived before 11am, Angela Berridge had beaten me to it. She had been with Thomas Wenleigh since 9.30 that morning – at his request. I smelled a rat.

At the meeting I accused MI5 of having bugged Special Branch's phones, not because they'd suspected Pollock of terrorist activities but because they routinely bugged Special Branch. Angela Berridge countered by maintaining that MI5 hadn't trusted Special Branch's security. Rather than telling her what a load of bollocks that was, I politely pointed out that MI5 had had no grounds for their suspicions. If they had had evidence that Special Branch wasn't secure, they should have made that evidence available so that Special Branch could have plugged the leaks. I was now warming to my theme. I told Wenleigh and Berridge that neighbours had reported that 'Hodges' had left his house just minutes before Pollock had arrived after the shooting. When Angela Berridge had given me a sheaf of photographs showing Pollock's arrival at the house, there had been none of 'Hodges' leaving – even though MI5 operatives had been in the area with cameras poised. It would seem that 'Hodges' had slipped straight through MI5's fingers. Just as DAC Gollap had predicted, he had vanished. I told both of them that I thought 'Hodges' had been with MI5, and that the whole incident involving Pollock and the MI5 break-in at the TA Centre was part of an elaborate plot to discredit Special Branch. I also told them that I suspected that the whole operation had been engineered by the Scarecrow.

Wenleigh had the grace to look embarrassed. He told both of us what a good job we had done and how now the whole investigation could be put to rest. The Minister would be making a statement about the shooting on television later that day. He thanked us for our help and we both left. I watched the Minister's speech with Mo, Harry and Commander Sullivan. All of us were left speechless. The Minister denied that any branch of the Security Services had been involved in the incident, and laid the blame entirely on Special Branch, while being outwardly sympathetic to the police and the hard job they have to do in a difficult situation. I was furious. I heard the phone ringing in my office and knew it was Molly. She was furious, too. She had reported the MI5 link and the Minister had dismissed it as 'infantile nonsense'.

Unable to let the case rest, I had to see Wenleigh again. I just couldn't let it alone. I caught up with him a couple of days later at Waterloo Place. It was a cold, blustery day and there weren't too many people around to observe us – just the pelicans in St James's Park. I confronted him about the official lies that had been told, and he told me not to be so silly and sensitive about the truth. He gave me a hypothetical example of a policeman giving secret information to the press, via a very pretty journalist, about an operation involving Her Majesty's Security Services. Wenleigh pointed out that the hypothetical policeman would be contravening Section 2 of the Official Secrets Act, and if evidence of such a disclosure was made available through a recorded telephone conversation, then such a man could lose his job, his pension, and spend several years behind bars.

I let Wenleigh go on his way, and I went into St James's Park. I didn't want to go anywhere near my office, my desk, knowing that MI5 had tapped my phone.

The investigation had left me feeling genuinely frightened. I am especially frightened now because I believe it could be the Scarecrow who is after me. After the investigation had been closed he just vanished. Wenleigh had guaranteed that the MI5 personnel who had been involved in the TA Centre incident would be severely censured for their actions. In fact, it had been me who ruined the Scarecrow's elaborate plans for discrediting Special Branch by exposing his plot to senior officials at the Home Office. Because of me he had failed. I'm sure he would like that failure avenged, and me silenced for good.

Suspect Dossier file No.: 14
Subject: DEPUTY CHIEF CONSTABLE BIRMAN

The investigation which took Mo, Harry and me to Nottingham had far-reaching consequences. We put into motion a chain of events which led to three senior police officers from the same division losing their jobs. No wonder public confidence in the police force is at such a low ebb.

We travelled up to the Midlands to investigate a demonstration which had turned into a riot. Apparently a group of around 1,500 demonstrators had been marching around the city's Town Hall, protesting against proposed cutbacks in the leisure amenities and social services. By all accounts it had been a good-natured demonstration – children, young mothers, nurses and OAPs had all taken part. Things had begun to go wrong, however, when one of the Councillors – I seem to remember that his name was Woods – came out on to the steps of the Town Hall to explain to the demonstrators why the cuts were necessary. The crowd had jeered him, so he decided to go in amongst the people and talk to them on a more personal level.

That was when the mood of the crowd turned ugly, and a few minutes later, apparently without warning, the Mounted Division came cantering around the corner to restore law and order. The result was like a replay of Peterloo – confusion, panic, screaming and injured people everywhere. The papers had reported four dead, and many more had been seriously injured.

At CIB, Graves informed me I wouldn't personally be heading the investigation into why the horses had been ordered in. The Police Complaints Authority was insisting that an expert in public order was brought in, and so Deputy Assistant Commissioner John Convey was in overall command. I was introduced to him in Graves's office. He seemed nice enough – a bit like Graves but with a sense of humour. He decided that the four of us – me, Mo, Harry and him – would travel up to Nottingham and stay there until the investigation was complete. As we walked to the canteen, Convey explained the guidelines for ordering Manoeuvre 11 – the deployment of horses to disperse a riot. According to police rules, the horses could only be cantered in if there was enough room for them to do so without causing injury or mass panic, if there was enough space to allow the crowd to disperse, and if there were no obstructions to impede their escape. In a nutshell, Manoeuvre 11 should only be used in serious rioting situations. The demonstration at the Town Hall hadn't been that. It would seem that a serious error of judgement had been made by the police. We were going to find out by whom and why.

We were met off the train at Nottingham by Assistant Chief Constable Jan Lewis, one of the highest ranking female officers in the country. I had heard of her, of course, but I had never met her before. She drove us to the police station via the Town Hall where the riot had taken place. It was a dismal sight. The place was deserted. Flowers and wreaths left out by the broken placards were being battered and washed away by the wind and rain. An old man was standing there – just as we drove past a policeman walked up to him and the old boy started crying, saying it was all the police's fault. Nobody in the car said anything. That was what we were up against.

Once inside the police station, we were led into an office which would be ours during the course of the investigation.

Mo, Harry and I grabbed coffees and an ashtray, and sat down to discuss what we had so far. We had been given a list of the senior officers at the station – the officers who were somehow responsible for the outcome of the demonstration. The Chief Constable was a man called Harmsworth. All we knew about him was that when the PCA had ordered an investigation into the riot, he had tried to bring in two of his mates from a neighbouring county to lead the investigation. He certainly hadn't wanted a CIB presence, and so we could be pretty certain that he would be hostile to us. We had already met ACC Jan Lewis, and the only remaining senior officer was Deputy Chief Constable Birman. Harry picked up on the fact that there was no acting Assistant Chief Constable for Operations. The existing ACC Ops had been off sick for two months and no temporary replacement had been appointed. In other words, there was no one in overall command to deal with riots and other public disturbances. If there had been someone in that position then the riot outside the Town Hall might well have never happened. Already our senior officers were beginning to look negligent.

The next officer in the pecking order was Chief Superintendent James Tattershall. He had been responsible for policing the demonstration outside the Town Hall, and it was he who had ordered Manoeuvre II. On paper, it looked as though we had our man, but nothing is ever that simple. Manoeuvre II always has to be authorised by a senior officer, and Tattershall hadn't been that officer. Although he had been the Duty Officer at the scene, the Duty Officer for that day had been DCC Birman. Tattershall would have had to have needed to get authorisation from Birman for Manoeuvre 11, yet it would seem Birman hadn't been at the Town Hall with him.

That was a good starting point for our investigations. I instructed Mo to talk to the Inspector of the Mounted Division, Harry to get to the hospital – Chief Constable Harmsworth was holding a press conference there at 5 pm and I wanted to hear exactly what he said – while I would interview Chief Superintendent Tattershall. We agreed to rendezvous at the local pub at 6 pm.

Convey interviewed Tattershall together with me. It felt strange to leave most of the questioning to another person; still, it was Convey who was officially leading the investigation. Tattershall was a nervous, twitchy man whose eyes seemed to be constantly blinking behind thick glasses. He filled us in on the background to the demonstration – the proposed council cutbacks, the bad feeling growing amongst the crowd. He had been expecting some 1,500 demonstrators, and had thought that he had enough troops on the ground for that number. However, he had then received reports that the demonstration was going to be infiltrated by leftist groups intent on inciting the crowd to attack the Town Hall. That was why the mounted police had been put on standby, and why the area surrounding the Town Hall had been cordoned off with metal barriers.

Tattershall maintained that he had deployed the mounted section when, in his opinion, the situation became dangerous to everyone: the anarchists had stirred up the mob, and Councillor Woods vanished into the crowd when all the earlier good feeling had evaporated. Tattershall felt he had gauged the situation correctly – he had been at the bottom of the Town Hall steps, right behind Councillor Woods, and had sensed the hostility of the crowd. At this point he decided to bring in the mounted section as children were in danger of being crushed. In his opinion there had been enough room for the crowd to disperse safely. Convey then asked him whether he had authority to send in the mounted section. After a moment's silence, Tattershall confirmed that he had – a general order had been made, giving him that authority. Although he was answerable to DCC Birman, Birman had been on police business elsewhere that day and Tattershall had been unable to get through to him, although he had tried on several occasions throughout the morning. As he couldn't contact his boss, he had to take action on his own. The decision to send in the horses had been his alone. We finished the interview there.

I met Harry as arranged at the Rising Sun at six. He was there with his brother-in-law. There was no sign of any flame-haired woman clutching a gin and tonic at the bar – Mo hadn't arrived yet. Harry gave me all his news. He had followed Harmsworth and the camera crew around the wards where the injured policemen lay. Harmsworth had successfully transformed his visit into a media circus, making a stirring speech about the brave officers who had tried to help the injured rioters and were in turn injured themselves. He defended the police, saying that they had been set upon by thugs from the militant left. Harry left it there and went to the ward where some of the injured rioters were. He knew he wasn't going to get an impartial view of events from Harmsworth and he wanted to find someone from whom he could. He ended up talking to a Mrs Furness. She was sitting at the bedside of her daughter, Christine, who was on a life-support machine – she had been crushed in the riot and was now in a coma. Mrs Furness told Harry they'd been standing right behind one of the metal barriers by the Town Hall, slowly getting crushed. She had asked a passing police officer whether she and her daughter could get through the barriers to escape the crush, but he had just told her to eff off. She had then decided that they would both have to fight their way back, away from the barriers and escape that way. It was then that she saw the horses and Christine went down. She told Harry that she had not heard any warnings. Mrs Furness hadn't been able to get to Christine – the crowd surged, there was confusion and panic everywhere. She had heard Christine screaming, but she couldn't reach her. She had felt helpless – and she felt helpless still. Harry left her holding her daughter's hand.

Harry, Joe and I ended up having quite a major session at the pub. By the time I'd left them I was totally pissed. I also felt guilty as I had told Mo that if I missed her in the pub I'd have dinner with her in the hotel dining-room. It was now far too late for that. As I staggered out of the cab a flame-haired beauty came to my aid. Mo told me I was pissed, I told her I was sorry, and she then told me I hadn't been missed anyway. I think I remember feeling quite hurt by that. While supporting me into the lift she gave me a run-down of her day's findings. I don't think she ever relaxed with me really. It appeared that down at the mounted section the injured horses were paraded in front of the press in much the same way that the injured police officers had been at the hospital. Mo had then chatted to an extremely unhelpful officer who wouldn't tell her anything other than that he had only been doing what he had been instructed to do.

It was later on, in the hotel dining room, that Mo's fun really began. She had been dining alone when a pretty blonde woman approached her and asked her whether she could join her. She then took control of the evening. She told Mo she was the MD of a haulage firm but was in Nottingham to attend a women's group get-together. The theme for the evening was 'Women and Careers', and the guest speaker was ACC Jan Lewis. Kate – Mo's friend – asked Mo if she'd like to come along, so she went. It proved to be a very interesting and enjoyable evening, and Jan Lewis had made an impressive speech. The only thing that spoilt it slightly was that ACC Lewis had been hostile to Mo afterwards.

I had a headache the following morning, but the three of us struggled through breakfast and drove down to the police station. We were greeted by the spectacle of Chief Constable Harmsworth giving yet another press conference. Obviously this was what the man specialised in. He issued a statement, declaring that the riot outside the Town Hall had been started by groups of anarchists who had cold-bloodedly set out to disrupt an orderly demonstration. Due to fine detective work, however, the anarchists had been traced and during the night arrests had been made. He held up leaflets that he claimed had been circulated for days before the riot which urged people to march upon the Town Hall, and he said that the various splinter groups went under the name of Class Struggle. All of that was news to us.

Harry and I went inside the police station. We were joined by Mo a few minutes later. She had some news to tell us. While Harmsworth's press conference was going on she had been approached by Councillor Woods, whom the police had blamed for exciting the demonstrators to the point at which a riot had become almost inevitable. He told her that he blamed Tattershall for the whole thing – the man had been worse than useless. Woods also told Mo that precautions just hadn't been taken. The demonstration had started really early in the morning, and there had been a carnival atmosphere to the whole proceedings. Stalls selling hot food and drinks had been set up down the side roads by the Town Hall, and kids could also buy toffee apples and balloons from the salesmen dressed as clowns. Tattershall had done nothing to clear the stalls and vendors; it was his fault that the roads around the Town Hall had been blocked, thus cutting off any means of escape for the fleeing demonstrators.

He also told Mo the police had arrested Tommy Burns, a Class Struggle activist. The man was in his late sixties, and more of a pain in the arse than a militant threat. In fact Burns was very good to people less fortunate than himself – he'd always champion their causes, filling in forms for those who felt confused by such things and generally helping people out. He was a pillar of the local community. Everyone knew him. Equally, because Tommy had been hauled in and arrested, everyone knew a cover-up was in progress; the police were looking for a scapegoat.

It was soon our turn to meet Tommy Burns. He was brought up from the police cells to be interviewed by Mo and me. A likeable old sod, he told us that on the previous evening, when he'd been sitting in his parlour reading a paper, armed police had barged in and arrested him. He didn't take to me very much – he said I was too soft and middle-class; and it was obvious that things had always come easily to me. If only he knew. He liked Mo. It must have been her Scottish accent. Mine was too south-east English for his approval.

84

After the interview I went back into the office and put through a call to Angela Berridge. Recently we'd been getting on much better, and were even beginning to share the odd joke here and there. I could even ask for her help – within reason – and she would give it to me. It was for that reason I rang her. I wanted to ask her about Tommy Burns and how militant he really was. A few minutes later she got back to me, telling me that Tommy belonged to a dying breed who still believed class struggle was in the genes. He was hardly a threat to the Establishment, and it hardly merited the presence to arrest him.

The following day Convey and I resumed our interview with Tattershall. We asked him what he knew about Class Struggle, as it was beginning to be clear that the official line from the police was that the riot had been instigated by them. Tattershall was very twitchy. I then decided to lay into him – the man was hedging all his answers, and at least two other people I had spoken with blamed the riot on his incompetence. I put it to him that the demonstration only turned into a riot *after* the mounted police charge, that it had in fact been the police who were responsible for creating the riot and not some loony lefties. I then quizzed him about his decision not to clear the side roads, which I considered to have been a serious error of judgement. Finally I suggested that pressure on police barriers was Tattershall's definition of a riot. The man had nothing to say. Convey stopped the tape and concluded the interview.

It was now time to get tough with the mounted police – I was getting sick of all the pussyfooting around. Mo, Harry and I went down to the stables and told the Inspector in charge that now the pressure was off Class Struggle, the Mounted Division were next in the firing line. His attitude was the same as that of the officer Mo had interviewed a few days earlier. He told us that he had done only what he had been told to do. From where he was deployed – halfway down a side street – he couldn't see the demonstration, so that when he was ordered to charge he was horrified to see a carnival rather than a full-scale riot. Again, like others before him, he blamed Tattershall's incompetence for the resulting mayhem. It had, he said, been a tactical error to canter the horses into an area enclosed by barriers. In his opinion it would have been more effective to have walked the horses in much earlier in the day. The Inspector finished by telling us that horses and barriers just didn't mix. The crowd had had no way of dispersing when the mounted section had cantered in.

Back at the station, I tracked down Chief Constable Harmsworth and I asked him to arrange an interview between us and DCC Birman, the senior officer who should had been on duty that day. I wanted to know what had happened to him to make him absent from policing the Town Hall demo. Harmsworth was unhelpful. He refused to let me talk to Birman, saying that the man had just taken sick leave and was not to be disturbed. It struck me then that quite a lot of officers from that station were going down with sicknesses that prevented them from carrying out their duties. My suspicions had been aroused. I wondered why Harmsworth wanted the buck to stop with Tattershall – it was obvious to me that the Chief Constable didn't want me going anywhere near Birman. I guessed that that was for three reasons: first, Birman was a friend of his; secondly, Harmsworth didn't want his second-in-command to appear incompetent and negligent in the execution of his duties; and thirdly, he didn't want the whole mess to be moved a step closer to him. However, I couldn't conclude my investigation without interviewing Birman. I decided to ask yet another favour of the delicious Ms Berridge.

Rather than talk to her on the phone, I decided I would meet her for breakfast in London. I really wanted to see her again – and she seemed pretty pleased to see me, even first thing in the morning. I asked her if she could exert pressure on Harmsworth to make him release Birman to me. I also wanted to talk to the sick ACC Ops who had been absent from his job for over two months. I wanted to know what was wrong with him. Angela told me. It wasn't sickness. The ACC Ops had been suspended after an incident involving some of his officers and a rookie constable who had been the butt of a practical joke that had gone wrong.

One night the officers had pretended to be armed robbers, had taken the rookie hostage and had then stuck a gun into his mouth. The result was that the young man had suffered a nervous breakdown.

Harmsworth had kept that fact very well hidden from the investigation.

Angela then filled me in on some background gossip. The ACC Ops was Birman's protégé, while the officer who refused to let the matter die was ACC Jan Lewis. It was through her insistence that the man had been suspended. I then remembered Mo telling me that Tattershall was a protégé of Lewis's – both of them had come from Staff Services. There was obviously a lot of bad feeling and grudges circulating amongst the senior ranks at Nottingham.

I reluctantly left Angela and made my way back to Nottingham. At the police station I was greeted by an agitated Mo. ACC Lewis had come to her, wanting to be interviewed by us immediately, before Tattershall talked to the press. He was due to make a statement to the press at 11.30 am. Meanwhile, Convey was talking to Harmsworth in a locked office – neither Mo nor Harry had been invited to attend the interview. We talked to ACC Lewis, who told us the whole story. Instead of supervising the policing of the Town Hall demonstration, Birman had been skiving – he had spent the day getting pissed with Chief Constable Harmsworth at a county cricket match. Tattershall had tried to contact Birman by mobile phone at several points throughout the course of the morning, but because he was seen by Harmsworth and Birman as Lewis's man, neither the Chief Constable nor his deputy had much time for him. The mobile had been switched off. Tattershall was left out on his own. By ordering the horses in he had made a bad decision, but his senior officers were just as much to blame for the riot through their own negligence and irresponsibility.

Lewis further informed us that Birman was an alcoholic and a bully, vindictive and spiteful. Both he and Harmsworth were hoping Tattershall would carry the can for the whole incident. I tried to impress this information on Convey, but he wasn't interested. He was more concerned with the negative PR that would result from pulling down a chief constable and his deputy than in dealing with the truth. Like everyone else, he wanted Tattershall to take the rap.

Tattershall did take the rap. In his statement he made it clear that he had made a huge error of judgment when he had ordered the horses in, and that he alone was responsible for the subsequent events.

Of course, his career was over.

I was furious that everyone seemed happy to let Tattershall take the blame when in fact he was just covering for mistakes made by Birman and Harmsworth, who in my opinion had been criminally negligent. I was determined to get Birman some day.

As it was, Harmsworth and Lewis ended up by finishing each other off. When she threatened to expose Birman for what he really was, Harmsworth decided to ruin her. He did this by secretly leaking her personal file to a journalist on one of the national papers. In it were the details of her lesbian relationship with Mo's new friend, Kate, the MD of the haulage firm. The press made a meal of a gay-cop scandal – a female at that – and so Lewis quietly resigned. But Harmsworth's little trick of passing on the file to the press was eventually exposed, and he rapidly followed in Lewis's footsteps.

Birman never returned from his temporary sick leave. I heard that after our investigation he turned more and more to the bottle, and that on being told that I was going to be gunning for him, he took early retirement on the grounds of ill health. He blames me for having lost him his cushy job and, deranged by bitterness and alcohol, he is easily capable of embarking on a campaign of intimidation by sending me death threats, or even of carrying out those threats.

Suspect Dossier file No.: 15
Subject: STEVEN RIPLEY

I wasn't investigating Steven Ripley, but I reckon he still wants to do me in. He isn't even a police officer – he never has been. But he was deeply embroiled in the events that took place last September, and I still hold him at least partly responsible for what happened to Harry. I knew then as I know today that Ripley was just one of the puppets, and that the puppeteer is yet to be had, but if he hadn't given Harry that security job, knowing he was still a serving officer, Harry might well have been in CIB today, without all the grief and heartache that the past few months have dumped on him.

I had noticed that since Harry had found out about Joyce's illness he had become more distant and withdrawn from Mo and me. Really, I couldn't have expected anything else – I just assumed he wanted to spend more time with her. That explained why he was beginning to turn up late at the office nearly every day. I assumed the reason why his work was beginning to suffer was because of the worry and stress her illness was creating. To my eternal shame, I did nothing to help him. I wish I had known the truth – I really wish Harry had confided in me, but he's just not that sort of bloke. The reason why he was turning up late every day, the reason why he looked so ill, was because he was knackered. He was trying to do two jobs at once – the one with us at CIB during the day, and the other at night, at a security firm. He was moonlighting because he was desperate for more cash. Joyce's debilitating illness meant that in time she would need round-the-clock care and attention – Harry would never have put his Joyce in a hospice. The only way Harry could afford to do this was to take on two jobs. And, of course, he got found out.

Last September, Graves came into my office and asked me where Harry was. He wasn't around; he was late again, but as soon as he came in I told him Graves wanted a word. I thought it was going to be a petty reprimand over his lack of punctuality, so Mo and I were speechless when, a few minutes later, Harry came back into the office and began to clear his desk, supervised by Graves. We wondered what the hell was going on – it certainly looked as if Harry was going for good.

When Harry had gone Graves told us what had happened in his office. In the presence of Commander Sullivan he had formally informed Harry that he was under investigation for carrying on business without the knowledge or permission of his senior officers. A Superintendent Mortimer from Jupiter Street would conduct the investigation into his affairs. In the meantime, Harry would have to do administrative work down at another station. Mo and I were still shell-shocked. We really had nothing to say; we just felt so terrible. However, we still had to pretend it was business as usual, so we compared notes on our investigation into two police officers from Wheeler Street station who had been accused of stealing a couple of porcelain figurines from the scene of a sudden death. As it turned out, the seemingly unimportant investigation was to be of enormous help to Harry and us.

On paper, the investigation actually seemed rather dull and uninspiring. Sergeant Carol Webb and PC James Willitts had forced an entry into the house of a dead woman in

Carrick Street, at the request of Meals-on-Wheels and her neighbours, who hadn't seen her for a couple of days. When they had entered the bedroom they found her dead in her bed, and so Sergeant Webb had told PC Willitts to go out to the panda car and radio in the sudden death report. Willitts had followed the correct procedure and soon 15 Carrick Street was swarming with police, ambulance men and nosy neighbours. It was shortly afterwards that the figurines were reported missing by the dead woman's niece, who lived only a couple of streets away from her aunt and had come over on receiving notification of her death. As Webb and Willitts had forced entry into her house and had been the first officers at the scene of her death, they were the obvious suspects.

Mo and I drove to Wheeler Street nick and interviewed Carol Webb, a very sensible, straightforward woman who looked as if her house was more likely to be decorated with nice glass vases from Habitat rather than old porcelain dogs nicked from a dead woman. She confirmed that our facts were about right. I asked her why she made PC Willitts – a nineteen-year-old probationer – call in the sudden death report. I suggested that it would have been more appropriate if she – a section sergeant – had done it instead. She agreed with me and explained that Willitts was fresh out of Hendon and still wet behind the ears. The old woman in bed had probably been the first body he had ever seen – and it hadn't been a pretty sight. Her eyes were open, her teeth were out, and her bowels had voided. Webb sensed Willitts was going to be sick if he stayed in the room, so she sent him outside and asked him to radio in for assistance. By doing that he kept his dignity and was doing something useful as well. It also showed me that Carol Webb was a considerate woman. I liked her – she was kind.

Kindness was a quality which had been absent from my life for quite some time. At dinner the night before, Angela Berridge had said she didn't want to see me again. I know that at first I had really disliked her, but over the following months we had worked with each other on more and more occasions until I had found myself falling in love with her. Angela was elegant, and she seemed to be in complete command of herself. I liked that. She said she didn't love me, but last July, on the way back from an enquiry at GCHQ in Cheltenham, we stopped off at a pub and ended up staying the night, making love in the fifteenth-century guest room. I was now smitten, totally obsessed by her. But she had told me she had had enough – thank you and goodbye. I knew she wasn't telling the truth. I knew she loved me as much as I loved her – I just had to make her see that for herself. But on the evening before Harry's bombshell, Angela had walked out of a restaurant and, she said, out of my life. She hadn't shown me much kindness then.

After interviewing Carol Webb, Mo and I drove back to CIB. Webb's story had seemed straightforward enough, and when I had asked her whether she had noticed anything of value in the house her response had been sound – she'd been looking for signs of forced entry or a struggle, not assessing the value of the house's contents. However, Webb had been the only person alone with the dead woman; Willitts had only ever been in the house with his sergeant up until she had sent him outside. Whichever way we looked at it, she was the only suspect as she had been the only person with the opportunity to take the figurines. I was beginning to suspect that the old lady had sold off the statues without her niece's knowledge, and Mo agreed with me. Still, just to be on the safe side, I asked Mo to check out Carol Webb's police record. It was only a matter of tapping her details into the computer. Webb came up smelling of roses – she was an exemplary police officer. If she hadn't decided to suspend her career to have kids she would most probably be much higher up the career ladder by now. The only black mark in her book was an incident which had happened many years ago when she had been a WPC. She had smashed up a squad car while on duty and had been temporarily suspended from driving. It didn't sound like anything too damaging.

The day had been strange and horrible, and Mo and I were both exhausted. I told her to go home, but she told me she was meeting Harry for a drink at the Sports and Social Club. It was going to be a difficult time for him. She asked me to come along too – he could do with his Guv's support. I couldn't come that night. I had a date; sort-of. Looking back I think I went though a period of madness then. I was planning to spy on Angela Berridge. I had decided that that evening I was going to follow her home on the train – I knew she lived in Goring – and see exactly what sort of private life she led: what her husband, her kids and her house were like. Nothing was going to stop me. Not even my bagman's situation. At that stage I was past caring for anybody but myself. I wasn't a complete bastard though. The next day I rang Harry – he was at home – and asked him over to the local for a pub lunch. There I caught up with all his news.

He had already had a meeting with the Police Federation rep, who had advised him not to take the administrative work Graves had offered – it would have been an embarrassment to the top brass at CIB, and it would have been embarrassing for Harry as well. Instead the rep had suggested that he should go on sick leave; it wouldn't be too hard to arrange with his doctor, given the stress and worry brought about by Joyce's illness. I can imagine Harry was upset by that – he hadn't wanted to use his domestic troubles to solicit sympathy at work, but the rep had advised him to play all the cards he had. He had also suggested that Harry should walk before he was pushed; in other words, retire early on medical grounds. I ordered us both another pint; clearly Harry hadn't got to the end of his story. He had never been a single pint man, anyway.

By then, Harry had come to think that early retirement was his only course of action. He would leave before his case got to the Disciplinary Board. The previous evening, however, when he was having his drink with Mo, something happened which made him change his mind. He was ensconced in a cubicle in the Gents' toilet when he overheard Graves and a colleague talking about him. Graves was being ribbed by his friend about the stroke Harry had pulled – a CIB officer who was going to be investigated by the CIB. Graves had replied breezily that he wasn't worried; he knew the case wouldn't go to the Disciplinary Board because Harry would settle for early retirement on medical grounds. Just like Decking. Harry told me that it stuck in his throat – he couldn't bear the thought that people would be putting two and two together and coming up with five. He didn't want his name and reputation tarnished by canteen gossip and speculation that he was taking an early bath to cover up years of dodgy dealings. Harry was not a bent copper, and he wanted to make sure that everyone knew that. He decided to take his chances with the Disciplinary Board – the worst that could happen would be that he'd be thrown off the force; the best, that he would suffer a demotion, although his name would be cleared . He then asked me for my support. I told him he had it, but it was Graves' backing that he really needed. So Harry asked me to sound him out, as he was unsure whether Graves would give him a decent character reference at the Disciplinary board. I knew what he meant. Graves was hardly going to stick his neck out over this, but I agreed that I'd sound him out.

I then asked Harry about Joyce. Apparently she'd given him the only good laugh about the whole business. When he had told her what had happened she was relieved. She thought he had been stupid trying to hold down two jobs for her benefit, and even more stupid in not telling her what was going on. She'd known something was up – he had been looking so tired. She had finally come to the conclusion that he had found another woman – a Page-3 bimbo with big tits who didn't need to use walking sticks. To hear that he had been moonlighting and was now in danger of losing his job was actually a load off her mind.

I went back to the office after lunch to be greeted by Mo telling me not to bother taking my jacket off – we were going to Wheeler Street, where there had been a development in the stolen figurines case. The property had been recovered in a raid on a fence's lock-up, and the local CID had him under arrest. We were going to Wheeler Street to interview him. On the way down Mo imparted a far more interesting piece of information. She'd been doing her research into Sergeant Webb's car accident. In the official report WPC Webb had taken full responsibility for the accident by admitting to having driven carelessly, but Mo was impressed by the number of senior officers who had come out in support of her. The most glowing character reference of all had come from her Inspector. Inspector Graham Sullivan, now Commander at CIB. Our boss. How very interesting.

At Wheeler Street a DS Luke came over and told us that the fence had already been interviewed by him and had given him the burglar's name, so there was no point in our interviewing him again. Luke was now on his way out with a team to arrest the burglar. I said we'd go with him. By this stage in my career I had developed a highly suspicious nature, and all of DS Luke's information seemed a little too cosy and pat for my taste.

The arrest was really quite something to observe. Two squad cars pulled up outside the suspect's house, the troops spilled out and attacked his door with a sledge-hammer. Mo and I followed in their wake. Once inside the filthy living room they arrested the man – he was huge and put up an enormous fight, but in the end two officers pinned his hands behind his back and frog-marched him out to the waiting car. We all then returned to Wheeler Street. Significantly, neither Mo nor I travelled back to the nick in the car containing the suspect. In retrospect, it wasn't too difficult to work out how the conversation in that car went during the journey.

The suspect's name was David Morgan, and he was a violent slob with an IQ which must have been struggling to reach double figures. He admitted to the burglary straight away; almost before DS Luke had read him the charges. Luke then told him that if Morgan admitted to that burglary and some twenty others in the area then Luke would wipe the slate clean and would not do him for resisting arrest as well. I couldn't believe my ears. I actually thought it was Mo and me who were getting stitched up, and not David Morgan. deciding to step in, I asked Morgan about the Carrick Street burglary. He had learned his lines well. He told me what a shock it had been breaking in and discovering the old woman lying dead in her bed. I reminded him that he couldn't possibly have broken in – the house was so secure that the police had had to force an entry through the front door. Luke then chipped in on behalf of Morgan, whose brain was threatening to explode. He told me Morgan had recently been involved in so many local burglaries that he couldn't remember how he had broken into each individual house. Luke was setting Morgan up to clear Webb and Willitts, but since Morgan was certainly guilty of the other burglaries, and Webb and Willitts were almost certainly not guilty of stealing two poxy old ornaments, I didn't see any point in blowing the whole situation out of proportion by carpeting DS Luke. We went back to CIB. I had a meeting with Graves planned for that afternoon.

I have always maintained that Graves is a cold fish. He didn't disappoint me in my expectations. He told me he thought Mo should be Acting Inspector in Harry's absence and that he would give Harry a reference as requested. I could tell he meant that he would do the bare minimum so I laid it on the line, telling him that Harry was a mate who needed his bosses' support. Graves's reply was that he was disassociating himself from Harry because he didn't want his career damaged by any corruption scandals in his department. Cold-hearted bastard.

Meanwhile I decided to resolve my Angela Berridge fixation once and for all. It was eating away at me and I was beginning to find it really hard to concentrate on anything at all. I decided to tell her husband about us – how much Angela loved me and how willing I was to take on her and their two kids. I must have been temporarily insane. In the end I didn't do it. I followed the Berridge family to a nice pub by the Thames – a bit like the one where Angela and I had made love for the first time – and engineered a chance meeting at the bar. Through gritted teeth Angela introduced me to her husband and asked me to join them for a drink. Donald, her husband, bought me a pint. It was whilst I was sitting outside, talking to them and their kids, that I realised I was planning to fight a battle which I would only lose. The stakes were too high for Angela. Her family meant everything to her – even after only a fifteen-minute drink with them I could see that. And she had been telling the truth. She didn't love me. I had just persuaded myself that she did. I bought the Berridges another round and returned to London. I thought that I had seen Angela for the last time. God knows, I didn't have an inkling then as to how disastrous and destructive our next meeting would be.

I came into the office early on Monday morning, but Mo had beaten me in. She was really excited, and asked me if it would help Harry's hearing if Commander Sullivan were to give him a top-notch character reference. Of course it would, but I told her it was extremely unlikely that Sullivan would stick his neck out for the little people; after all, Graves had refused to do so. Mo disagreed, and then told me the reason for her excitement. When she had finished her story I was quite excited too. Mo, however, needed my help to make sure her information was to be of any practical use. So I agreed to blackmail Sullivan.

I arranged to meet Commander Sullivan at the National Portrait Gallery the following day – I told him that I had wanted to meet him away from the office as I wished to discuss a personal matter. We chatted about Harry for a while and then I told him a character reference from a senior officer would be extremely helpful. Sullivan knew I wasn't talking about Graves. He looked at me as I outlined a hypothetical case of an inspector being involved in a car accident after having had a few drinks too many. Carrying on with my story, I suggested that if a sober WPC who had been in the car with him was to take all responsibility for the accident, she would probably suffer a bit of temporary grief but nothing too damaging or permanent. I then put it to Sullivan that the WPC would have saved the Inspector's career, and went on to say that should such a story get out years later, that officer, having dumped on the WPC, would no longer command the respect of his subordinates. Without the support of his troops, and with other rumours spinning off the crash story, the officer's career would stall and he couldn't really expect to climb any higher in the service.

It was then that Sullivan told me to shut it or he'd report the conversation. He walked off. I knew I'd won.

Good old Mo. While I had been busy making a tit of myself at the weekend, she'd been working hard. She hadn't been impressed by the outcome of the Wheeler Street enquiry and had wanted the full story of Carol Webb's car accident – from Carol Webb herself.

The two women had met on Saturday afternoon in a West London patisserie. Mo asked Carol Webb to let her know, off the record, what had really gone on with the stolen figurines – she really hadn't bought David Morgan's story. Webb told her that she and Willitts hadn't responded to the shout together. They were in the area of Carrick Street, interviewing a couple of householders, when the call came through. Webb told Willitts to answer it because she wanted to finish the interview. Unfortunately Willitts was a bit too enthusiastic and instead of examining the outside of the house for signs of forced entry, he took it upon himself to investigate the inside as well. When he found the body he lost his bottle and ran back to Webb. It took her ten minutes to calm him down. When he was composed they went back into the house together. By that stage it had been left open and unattended for more than a quarter of an hour. Anybody could have walked in off the street and taken the figurines – and, obviously, someone had. Webb had then lied in her report in order to protect Willitts – he was only a probationer, after all.

Mo had then pushed Carol Webb even further. She said that she was willing to forget the fact that Webb had deliberately filed an incorrect report if she told her what had happened all those year ago, when Inspector Sullivan had stood up for her over the car accident. The rest, as they say, is history.

We told Harry the good news in the pub later on that evening. It was a couple of days before his Disciplinary Board, so he was really choked that we'd gone to so much trouble on his behalf. He then dropped another bombshell on us. He said he hadn't told anybody the full story. Something dodgy had gone down one evening at the security firm where he had been moonlighting. Furthermore, he suspected the current mess he was in was connected with that incident.

He had been in the control room of High Security Express, monitoring alarm systems for offices all over town, when a maintenance man had come in to do some work – he had been instructed by the MD, Steven Ripley, to disconnect one of the security alarms belonging to a company which used the services of High Security Express. When Harry had asked him to note the job down in his log book, the man refused, saying everything had been taken care of and his visit was not to be recorded. He told Harry it had all been squared up – someone had made a mistake and now that mistake was being quietly covered.

The next day Harry was given a £500 bonus to keep silent.

I blew up at him, I was so bloody furious. I couldn't believe how bloody stupid he had been. There we were, Mo and I, blackmailing the Commander into giving Harry a reference which made him sound like Mary Poppins, while he was busy accepting backhanders from High Security Express. If he was really unlucky and the story got out, Harry could be done for criminal offences, never mind the Disciplinary Board.

Mo was altogether much calmer. She asked Harry the name of the company whose alarm had been turned off. The next day she paid a visit to McNicholl & Flowers, Solicitors, to see whether they had been done over. They hadn't. The receptionist informed Mo that the last time the police had been called in was over the theft of a handbag, over a year ago.

Mo had come up with nothing and I was beginning to sense a cover-up. The smell of it was becoming increasingly familiar, too. It stank of MI5 involvement.

On the morning of Harry's Disciplinary Board I paid a visit to the offices of High Security Express. I wanted to talk to the boss, Steven Ripley. It was early in the morning, quiet, so no one was around when I grabbed the bastard, pushed him up against one of his own security vans and roughed him up a bit. He deserved what he got. Because of him and his dodgy business Harry was going to lose a job and I was going to lose the best deputy I'd ever had. I slammed him against the van again and asked him what the hell was going on – why were security alarms being quietly taken off-line? Ripley didn't know. As far as he was concerned everything had been sanctioned. I threatened to have the depot turned over by the police. He understood that that would be bad for business – even a hint of malpractice at a security firm would drive his clients elsewhere. He knew I could ruin him. I asked him what he had meant when he said the operation had been 'sanctioned'. That word rang alarm bells of its own; it sounded suspiciously MI5 to me. Ripley told me he had a security consultant who dealt with that side of things. His name was John Deakin. I let Ripley go. He sank to the ground.

With half an hour to go before the start of Harry's Disciplinary Board, I shot round to Deakin's offices; I knew I had to face up to him again. I stormed past his glamorous, plush secretary into his glamorous, plush office. He was obviously doing well for himself in private enterprise after his stint in the public sector. I didn't bother sitting down. I told him that what he had done was despicable – he had implicated Harry in some shady deal of his and then had grassed him up, just to get back at me.

Deakin told me to piss off; that if I suspected him of some criminal activity then I should prove it. However, he doubted whether I'd get anything on him; as ever, he was fireproof. I should have learnt that by now. He did say that in terms of what Harry had done at the security firm – turning a blind eye to irregular practices – he was fireproof too. There would be no comeback from any quarter for that. The man was oozing confidence and I wanted to smash his face in. Although I couldn't prove it, I suspected that Deakin had been using the facilities offered by High Security Express to do a job for MI5 – the one Harry had uncovered. If Deakin was now working for MI5 then that was grim news for me. I knew I wasn't their favourite police officer and had suspected for some time that my office and home phones were both being tapped. I also suspected that on occasion I was being followed. Or maybe I was just being paranoid.

Deakin's parting shot confirmed all my suspicions. He told me that if he ever got around to settling old scores, he'd be going for the engine driver and not the oily rag.

I arrived late at Harry's Disciplinary Board – he'd already been found guilty of working without his superiors' knowledge or permission, but his solicitor was now pleading for clemency prior to Harry's punishment being pronounced, and was asking for the Board to take into account the mitigating circumstances and the character references from Harry's superiors. As I arrived Graves was just finishing his character reference. It was as bloodless as I expected – there was nothing personal in Graves's summing-up of Detective Inspector Harry Naylor. To compensate Graves's performance I really went to town on mine, telling the Board that Harry was loyal, diligent and scrupulously honest. I left them in no doubt that I had no higher regard for any other officer I had ever worked with, even when we had conflicting interests. The thing was, I didn't have to make up a word. It as all true. Harry was the best.

It was then Commander Sullivan's turn. He didn't let us down. He told the Board he was eager to offer his support, since the troops at the sharp end often felt isolated from or even discarded by their senior officers. He gave Harry one of his famous glowing references.

The outcome could have been much worse – Harry could have been thrown out of the police force and his pension could have been forfeited. As it was his punishment was still pretty harsh – demotion to the rank of sergeant, a fine equivalent to three months' pay, and a transfer out of CIB. It wasn't as bad as being told he'd be directing traffic for the rest of his life, but he had lost a job he had been good at, and I'd lost an excellent deputy and colleague. We all came out losers on that one.

As a result of my treatment of Steven Ripley – walking all over him and kicking the shit out of him – he must surely hate me enough to want me dead. He's stupid enough to try and put the frighteners on me – perhaps for his own personal satisfaction or maybe as part of a grander scheme. Maybe MI5 is behind all of this. Maybe they're hoping the death threats will act like a nudge in the back to push me into a situation where they can really stitch me up. Wherever I go and whatever I do from now on, I'll check and back-up and double-check everything. Like Deakin and the rest of them, I'm going to make sure I'm fireproof.

SUMMARY

Of course, people like me are never fireproof. Deakin did get me in the end – he got me, rather than the other way round because he's an animal, a predator with no sense of morality or decency or pity. He studied me and then got me in my Achilles Heel – my infatuation with Angela Berridge. During the hot summer our affair had been as torrid as the weather, and Deakin had gained possession of all the photographs which proved that – plus tape-recordings of our nights together and one X-rated video. I must remember to order up a copy from MI5.

Just when I thought I really had him, he fought his way out of the corner into which he had been boxed by promising me that if I brought him down he'd make sure Angela Berridge went down with him. Angela then confirmed that he could do it. You see, they had been working together – MI5 and Deakin. I wonder now whether Angela had really ever enjoyed her time with me, or whether when she had been screaming my name out loud, it was MI5 and her sense of duty which was playing around in her head. I don't think I'll ever know.

She – and the organisation for which she works – did come to my rescue when I was arrested for the murder of a man – a situation which had been engineered by Deakin, naturally. He was – still is – the puppet-master, and he pulled my strings until even I didn't know what the hell was happening. The outcome was that armed police found me covered in blood in a house in London, with a man – a Special Branch informant – dead at my side, and a gun in my hand. Deakin's gun – although it was untraceable to him. I was instantly arrested, but MI5 arranged it so that I was released in a matter of days. They couldn't afford to let me go down screaming. I knew too much.

From the previous reports, of course, you can see that it's not just MI5 who have a special interest in me. Those who would want to see me dead exist in depressing abundance. If I'm found floating face down in the Thames, riddled with bullets, this dossier might give the investigating officer somewhere to start. On the other hand, if the investigating officer ever crossed my path while I was with CIB, this dossier may well end up rotting in the river, too.